More Praise for *Fit to Suc*

Steve's core message—that skyrocketing healtl
an opportunity for those companies that choose
manage the risk—is brilliantly delivered throu;
Forward-thinking CEOs will take action. Thos
leaving large sums of money on the table.
Robert L. Cohen, CEO
The IMA Financial Group, Inc.

As medical costs continue to rise at staggerii
Succeed challenges business leaders to think d
health insurance. This book is a must-read if
taking bad news on health insurance premiums
board every year.
David Brooks, Chairman and CEO
Independent Bank Group

Fit to Succeed proves that turning healthcare
ernment and throwing money at the problem
tion. Proactive risk management and person;
are the keys to success.
Greg Wilkinson, CEO
Hill & Wilkinson, Ltd.

Steve is out to change the way we view healthc;
America. *Fit to Succeed* reflects his passion, prog
and years of experience in the field. The creativ
makes this informative and practical book a fur
Steve's been practicing what he's preaching for
Dr. Jeff Warren, Tri-athlete and Pastor
1st Baptist Church of McKinney, Texas

Having coached over 13,000 entrepreneurs, I
of the competitive pressures they face. By pr
tools and insights, *Fit to Succeed* takes on a
ballooning healthcare costs—and transforms ;
tive advantage.
Dan Sullivan, President and Founder
Strategic Coach®

FIT TO
SUCCEED

FIT TO
SUCCEED

make health and wellness your
competitive advantage

STEVE HEUSSNER

NH Publishing LLC, Dallas

ISBN 978-0-9814527-2-2

Publisher's Cataloging-in-Publication data
Heussner, Steven J.
   Fit to succeed : make health and wellness your competitive advantage / Steve J. Heussner.
   p. cm.
   ISBN 978-0-9814527-2-2 (hardcover)

1. Employee health promotion. 2. Health education. 3. Health promotion. 4. Occupational Health Services. 5. Physical fitness. 6. Health facilities—Risk management. I. Title.

RC969.H43 H38 2008
613.20—dc22   2008921424
First Edition

NH Publishing LLC
12222 Merit Drive, Suite 1560
Dallas, TX 75251
USA

Printed in Canada

To my wife, Risa, and my children, Kimberly and Eric.
Without your love and support, this book
would not have been possible.

To my parents, Lloyd and Esther Heussner,
who taught me to love, to live and to work.

CONTENTS

PART III: THE SEARCH FOR EVIDENCE

PART IV: THE FINAL CHALLENGES

Getting into Shape: The Real-Life
Method

Introduction

The time for corporate America and ordinary Americans to sit up and take charge of their healthcare is now. In my years working with healthcare insurance, I've witnessed a system in decline, a system that is getting more expensive and less effective by the day. Fortunately, I've also encountered people who—like me—have the ideas and the initiative to propose changes to the system. These changes have already been implemented by certain forward-looking business leaders, and they have been proven to work.

A huge part of the reason some businesses—the ones that aren't so forward-looking—are at a crisis point with their healthcare insurance is that they're still operating according to an outdated model. This reactive model is one in which every player in the game is compensated on a percentage of premiums: the insurance brokers, the doctors, the hospitals, and the drug companies. The sicker Americans get, the richer these people get. So it's no wonder that none of these players have any reason to want the system to change.

But what about business leaders whose workforces have been rendered increasingly ineffective because employees are overweight, out of shape, and consequently way more susceptible to a whole raft of life-threatening diseases? And what about the workers themselves?

Neither the business leaders nor the workers are gaining anything through higher premiums for healthcare insurance. So the push for change has to come from them— from business leaders who want to get a competitive edge, stop pouring money into soaring healthcare insurance, and enjoy higher profits, and from ordinary Americans who want to feel in control of their health again.

Through my many years in the insurance system, I have seen up close how the old system—the reactive model—doesn't work. That experience has inspired me to come up with a better model for handling healthcare insurance—a proactive model. This healthcare-plan risk-management program will make a difference in the lives of both business owners and employees. That's why I call it a win–win situation.

Throwing money at the problem is not the answer. Looking to government is not the answer. Proactive risk management *is* the answer. This book is about gaining a competitive advantage through proactive healthcare-plan risk management. Those who understand this will be the ones with the competitive advantage.

You might be thinking, "Isn't the current reactive model so entrenched that it will be a very difficult job to change anything?" It's true that any change can appear intimidating at first and that many people have a psychological aversion to it. That's why it's essential for CEOs and their upper management to set the example and embrace change.

My proactive model boils down the process of change to seven manageable steps. They are illustrated in the story that follows. The characters are fictional, but the process itself is inspired by real life.

I hope that seeing the seven steps broken down in this way will inspire readers at both management and non-management levels to push for change in their companies.

The fictional companies here are inspired by the construction industry, which is one with which I've worked closely. But the model is the same for whatever kind of business you operate or work in.

I sincerely hope that this book will inspire readers to wake up and take personal and corporate responsibility for bringing the healthcare crisis under control.

There is a way to make a difference, and you are an integral part of the solution.

A CEO FINDS THE ROAD TO WELLNESS:

———

A PARABLE

An Awakening

Walt Williams was used to success. At age sixty-four, he had achieved a lot and wore the badge of his achievements with great pride. Happily married for close to thirty-five years, he was the father of two grown children who were well established in life. As CEO of Midland Building Associates, a multimillion-dollar construction company based in Phoenix, Walt flew from state to state in the firm's private jet, overseeing projects. After many years of success, Walt wasn't expecting anything to ruin the road map he had carefully laid out for his life, certainly not something as seemingly unconnected to his career as what his employees ate for breakfast. If only Walt had known what steps he could have taken to save himself a whole lot of grief—and money.

PART I

PROBLEMS
ARE BREWING

Chapter 1: A Joint Venture

Mike (Miguel) Lopez and Walter F. Williams were both CEOs of large construction companies in the southwestern United States. They were both in their early sixties and both highly successful at what they did, spearheading deals worth hundreds of millions of dollars a year. Construction ran in each of their families.

Mike's father, Pedro, had grown up in a well-to-do family in Mexico City and came to Texas to study. With his gift for engineering and a sizable inheritance, Pete (as he called himself in the States) had founded Cora Construction Ltd., in Austin, Texas, in the 1950s. Walt's dad, Stanley, was also an immigrant. He'd come to the United States from Ireland after the First World War. He had started off in construction in a small two-man operation in Chicago, but it had grown into a larger company called Midland Building Associates, and eventually Stan had been able to buy out his partner. He had decided to relocate to Phoenix because he really enjoyed the climate.

Little did Pete Lopez and Stan Williams imagine that one day their sons would be hatching a business deal together. Personality-wise, Mike and Walter couldn't have been more different.

Walt was gregarious and outgoing—some even called him arrogant. He was highly competitive and made a lot of business decisions based on gut instincts. He was loyal but could also come across as sounding highly critical. Sometimes this was expressed in harsh words. But Walt was fundamentally a decent guy. If he lost his temper and flew off the handle, he was quick to admit his mistake and apologize.

Mike was definitely the more cautious of the two. "Slow and steady" was his motto. He liked to weigh all the options before making a decision and committing himself to a course of action. Some associates found this tedious at times, but Mike was confident in his approach. Like Walt, he was competitive. But unlike Walt, he channeled that competitiveness into athletics as well as business.

Despite these personality differences, Mike and Walt had a lot of mutual admiration. Over the years, they had gotten to know each other quite well, meeting up regularly at conferences and workshops organized by national and regional construction associations. Mike enjoyed Walt's sense of humor. And Walt liked Mike's steadiness of hand.

They also respected each other's business acumen. Mike and Walt were both astute enough to know when it was to their companies' advantage to join forces to bid on construction projects that they were more likely to win with pooled resources. Construction is a risky business, and it's never a good idea to commit too much of your assets to one job.

And this is what brought the two CEOs together on a warm autumn evening in Austin. They were putting the finishing touches on a joint-venture bid for a $300 million-dollar highway interchange in Dallas.

Chapter 2: The Night Before

It was about 8:30 P.M. The next morning, a highway letting was scheduled to take place at the Blue Moon Hotel,
in the ballroom overlooking Lady Bird Lake. (A letting,
as it is known in the business, is the name given to the
process of awarding state construction projects by competitive bid.) These lettings took place on a monthly basis,
and the executives who took part in them were familiar
with the routine. In the space of a couple of hours, companies submitted their bids, transportation-department
officials analyzed them, and then the winning bids were
announced. The projects were often worth hundreds of
millions of dollars, so adrenaline ran pretty high at the
lettings.

Both Mike Lopez and Walt Williams enjoyed this
part of their jobs and felt right at home at the Blue Moon.
Over the years, they'd taken part in many highway lettings here. The poised staff at the four-star hotel knew
the CEOs and greeted them by name. Walt had flown in

from Phoenix on his company jet that morning and was comfortably ensconced in his favorite corner suite, the one that was always reserved for him when he passed through town.

Walt was meeting Mike at the Lakeview Bar, just off the main lobby. They were going to hammer out the final details of the joint-venture bid they were submitting the next day for the Dallas interchange. The bartender, Xavier, nodded hello. He knew what to pour them even before the two men had had time to slip into the deep, suede-covered armchairs in their favorite corner by the fireplace. A glass of merlot for Mr. Lopez and a single malt for Mr. Williams. Walt liked Xavier to surprise him with a different choice from the bar's impressive whiskey collection.

"Xavier, my man," Walt said cheerily as the bartender approached them with his tray. "What have you got for me tonight?"

"It's a sixteen-year-old single malt, sir. Sherry-matured."

Walt picked up the tumbler and took a long whiff and then a taste.

"Oh, yes. This is fine indeed. An excellent choice."

Xavier nodded and walked away with a satisfied smile.

Mike, however, appeared worried as he took a sip of his wine. Walt, who was always on the lookout for any excuse for a good-natured poke in the ribs, picked up on it.

"Hey, Mike," he said, "I can tell you're at the Blue Moon because you look like you're on the moon." Walt chuckled. "What's the matter? I thought you liked the pressure cooker of highway lettings."

"You know I do, Walt," Mike replied. "But this time, I can't quite put my finger on it. I don't have a good feeling about tomorrow."

"Don't you worry, Mikey boy," Walt said in his usual booming voice, full of self-confidence, as he slapped Mike on the back. "We've got this baby wrapped up."

"Well, you've got a pretty good track record," Mike responded. "I sure hope you're right. Because clinching this interchange deal would suit my business plans just fine."

For the next forty minutes, the two men sat hunched over their papers. They spoke in hushed tones. Mike had pulled out his laptop and was inputting some data. When they got to the end of the stack of documents, Mike started to close up his keyboard.

"I hope you don't mind if I turn in early," he said. "That way, I can squeeze in a workout before the letting starts tomorrow."

Walt smiled. He knew that Mike was a fitness nut.

"Hey, Walt," Mike added. "You really should try the gym here. The Blue Moon has amazing sports facilities, you know."

Walt laughed. "How would I know that, Mikey? I leave all that spa stuff up to the gals."

Mike shrugged his shoulders and grinned.

He waved good-bye and left the hotel lobby to get his bike, which he'd locked up outside the front gate. As much as possible, Mike preferred to get around Austin on two wheels instead of four.

Walt signaled to Xavier for another single malt.

Chapter 3: How Mike Starts the Day

The morning of the highway letting dawned a gorgeous September day, with the kind of freshness in the air that gave an extra jolt of energy to all those who were up early, getting some exercise before heading off to work. Mike, as usual, was one of them. He was in the habit of setting his alarm for 5:30 A.M., so he'd have time for a workout before getting down to work, even on busy days. He found it helped clear his mind and calm his nerves. The weather was so nice that Mike decided to bypass the excellent gym next to his office to go for a run on the recreation trails along Lady Bird Lake. He had to go right by the grounds of the Blue Moon to get to the trail. Lacing up his running shoes, he tried to quell the feeling of unease about the bid that he and Walt would soon submit. But as soon as he started running, the tension dissipated from his body, as it usually did.

Other people had had the same idea as Mike that morning. Despite the early hour, the trail buzzed with runners, bikers, and in-line skaters. Rowers were out on the water. And even the birds swooping overhead seemed relaxed.

After his five-mile run, Mike made his way up to the eighteenth floor of the Commerce Building, where Cora Construction had its headquarters, and he took a quick shower. He had been sure to have shower facilities installed when the company moved in five years ago.

Then Mike went to the office kitchen to make himself some breakfast. He had the same thing every morning: a protein shake. But he liked to vary the ingredients. Today it would be mixed berries and flaxseed, he decided. He lined everything up on the counter and measured it out into the blender. As he pushed the power button, he tried to lose himself in the whirring of the motor, to hold on to the feeling of calm that running had given him.

Mike had always been an athlete. But he had never clearly understood the importance of post-workout nutrition—that is, until his wellness program advocate had advised him that proper nutrition and exercise would give him positive energy so that he could be his most productive and creative. From his wellness advocate, Mike learned that the body needs protein, vitamins, and minerals thirty to forty-five minutes after a workout. Feeding the body the right things at the right time builds strength and provides the energy necessary to have a productive and creative day.

Chapter 4: How Walt Starts the Day

Even with his alarm set for 8:30 A.M. and a wake-up call ordered, Walt had trouble rousing himself. The night before, after Mike had headed home, Walt had ended up running into a bunch of acquaintances from the construction business who had dropped by the Lakeview Bar. They had got to talking, had a couple more rounds, and then stepped out into the refreshing night air for a cigar. Before he had known it, it was close to midnight.

When Walt had got up to his room, he'd reached for the remote and flipped on the television. It was always the first thing he did whenever he got in, whether at home or at a hotel. Zapping through the channels, he'd discovered that one of his favorite films was on: Roman Polanski's *Chinatown*. It wasn't just the film noir ambience that he loved, nor just the standout performances by Jack Nicholson and Faye Dunaway. It was the fact that this was the story of a construction project, a mystery centered on Los Angeles' famed water-supply system. It had been ages since Walt had last seen *Chinatown*, and he hadn't been able to resist the temptation to watch it again, even if he did have a full day ahead tomorrow.

Walt cracked open the minibar, poured himself a Scotch and opened a can of potato chips.

"Damn. Those cigars sure do open up the appetite," he said to himself with a chuckle. He then settled in to watch the film.

By the time the credits rolled, it was already 2:30 A.M. But Walt had fallen asleep with a grin. He'd had a good feeling about the next day. He was sure he'd find himself with a profitable new project for his company.

He wasn't feeling quite so chipper, though, at 8:30 when his bedside alarm began blasting and the phone started ringing with his wake-up call. Walt was very tempted to roll over and grab another hour or so of sleep, but he forced himself to climb out of bed.

Highway lettings waited for no man—not even Walt Williams. There was a strict schedule to adhere to. He stumbled to the coffee machine to get it started and picked up the phone to order a room-service breakfast. He hadn't even looked at the menu. But he was famished and knew exactly what he wanted.

"Good morning, Mr. Williams," the room-service operator answered. "And how are you this fine morning?"

"Well, frankly, I could do with some more shut-eye," Walt replied. "But a big steaming pot of your strongest coffee will help. With cream."

"And what else would you like, sir?"

Walt went through the list in his head. "Three eggs, scrambled. Lots of home fries. Ketchup. White toast with plenty of butter."

"Any meat with that, sir?"

"Yeah. How about some of everything? Bacon, sausages, ham. The works. I could eat a horse this morning."

"Coming right up, sir."

With the thought of breakfast spurring him on, Walt dragged himself off into the shower to finish waking up.

Chapter 5: A Huge Disappointment

By 10 A.M., Mike and Walt met up in the Blue Moon's ballroom after submitting their bid for the Dallas interchange. There were a couple of hours to kill before the results would be announced, and both men took advantage of the time to do some networking with their colleagues from the construction industry.

By 11:30, the bar had opened up outside the ballroom, as was customary at construction lettings. The Blue Moon's house specialty was a mean Bloody Mary, and a bartender stood behind the counter, pulling out celery and salting glasses as he whipped up the cocktails.

"Hey, Sammy," Walt said as he strode up to one of the familiar servers. "How about you make a couple of special drinks for me and my business partner?"

Mike just happened to be walking by, and Walt pulled him up to the bar.

Sam, the bartender, smiled as he reached for a second glass, but Mike stopped him before he could get it.

"Not for me, thanks," Mike said.

"Aw, Mikey," Walt patted him on the back. "You should relax and live a little."

Both men continued their networking until a voice at the microphone announced that lunch would be served. The winning bids for the projects up for grabs would be revealed after the meal.

Walt and Mike sat down side by side at a round dining table. It was a traditional lunch on the menu today: medium-rare rib-eye steaks, mashed potatoes and gravy, creamed corn, and onion rings. Their manner of approaching the meal was as different as their styles of doing business and organizing their personal lives. Walt dived right into the food with great gusto, whereas Mike was more deliberate, taking a bite here and there at a slower pace. When chocolate cheesecake was served for dessert, Walt embraced it with relish whereas Mike motioned to the server that he didn't want any.

As the waiters made their way around the tables with pots of coffee, the large screens dominating the ballroom suddenly came to life, hissing and sparking as though somebody were switching channels on a television.

A woman's smooth voice came on. "Ladies and gentlemen," she said. "We're pleased to announce the results of today's highway letting."

One by one, the projects at stake were called out. For each one, the winning bid and the second-place bid were projected. The tradition was to always show the second-place bid so the winners knew how much they had left on the table and the runners-up knew by how much they needed to sharpen their pencils.

Finally, after what seemed like an eternity to Mike and Walt, the Dallas interchange was up. Walt turned to Mike and gave him a big thumbs-up.

"And the contract goes to . . ." the woman's voice read out, "Murphy and Sons from Houston, Texas, coming in at $301 million. And second place goes to the Cora–Midland joint venture at $305.5 million."

Chapter 6: What Went Wrong?

It was clear from their expressions that both Mike and Walt were crushed by the news they'd just heard. But each man put on a brave face for the sake of appearances in front of all the other CEOs. It seemed like forever till they managed to escape the crush of industry chatter that erupted in the Blue Moon ballroom after the bid results were announced. But finally, Mike and Walt found a moment alone in a corner, and they agreed to meet at Peterman's Steak House in half an hour.

Peterman's was just a short distance away from the Blue Moon. It was a local landmark. And ironically, although Mike was the one who lived in Austin, it was Walt who was a Peterman's regular. Whenever he was in town, he was sure to drop by, drawn by its cozy atmosphere, world-famous martinis, and fantastic steaks. The staff at Peterman's knew him well, just like those at the Blue Moon.

"Let me give you a lift, Mikey," Walt said as they emerged into the lobby and approached the valets.

Mike said, "Naw, it's okay, Walt. I'll walk over there. It helps me clear my mind. Why don't you leave your car behind and walk with me?"

"Naw, Mike, I don't really feel like walking," Walt muttered.

Mike answered, "C'mon, Walt. Just walk with me. You'll feel better."

He was so forceful in the way he said it that Walt knew it wasn't worth his energy fighting back. So he shrugged his shoulders and strode off with Mike.

Thirty minutes later, the two men were sitting in a booth at the back of the restaurant, dissecting the bid they had failed to win.

"Seems I've been losing more than my fair share of bids lately. I'm wondering if there's any funny business going on with the process," Walt muttered. He was so mad that the redness of his face was noticeable even in the dim lighting of the restaurant.

"Hey, Walt. The system is foolproof, you know," Mike replied. He looked much calmer than Walt, although his eyes did betray what he was feeling. But it was also obvious that Mike's mind was hard at work and that he had a pretty good idea of why they didn't get the bid.

"Walter," Mike started to say. Walt sat up straighter, responding to the unusual circumstance of hearing his name in full.

"Walt," Mike continued, "I think the best way to approach this is for each of us to go away to our offices and drill down into the bid. Each of us will analyze it, line by line, to see where we might have been quoting too high a figure and why we got beat."

Though Walt didn't generally like this kind of analytical process, preferring to go with his gut reactions, he had to agree with Mike that this time it sounded like the right course of action. They decided to touch base again in exactly a week to go over what they found.

Chapter 7: Mike Drills Down

The morning after the highway letting, Mike was up early, as usual. He biked to his gym for a workout, then rode over to his office. It was only 7:00 A.M., and he was one of the first people in.

He dropped his saddlebag onto his desk and changed out of his biking clothes into one of the number of suits he kept at work. Then he wandered over to the office kitchen. To outsiders, it might seem like a fairly insignificant detail, but having a kitchen stocked full of healthy food for his employees was one of Mike's proudest professional achievements. His pet peeve was the compulsion for unhealthy snacking at the office, the urge to gorge on doughnuts in the morning, hamburgers at lunch, chocolate bars in the afternoon. It drove him crazy not only because of how much it hurt the health of his employees but also because of how much it hurt the profit margin of his company. Decreased productivity. Higher healthcare costs. Higher absenteeism.

Mike was surprised that most CEOs didn't seem to pay this any notice.

So ever since he'd taken over the reins of Cora Construction from his father, Mike had made it a point to have a fridge full of fresh fruit and low-fat yogurt and a cupboard full of nuts and low-calorie granola bars. He looked at the fruit selection this morning with satisfaction and decided on a blueberry–banana smoothie.

Just as he was powering up the blender, he heard footsteps outside. It was his assistant, Suzanne, her happy face still flush from her own morning workout. She waltzed into the kitchen area to make herself a shake. The office kitchen nook was a popular place to fuel up for the day ahead.

"Hey there," Mike greeted her. "How are you doing this morning? Good workout?"

"Excellent, boss," Suzanne replied.

"Great stuff," Mike said. "Now take your time and get settled in, but when you are, could you set up an appointment with Hartley?" Hartley Smith was Cora's healthcare-plan risk-management consultant. It was Hartley who had transformed Cora from the old reactionary healthcare model to the new proactive risk-management platform on which it thrived.

Suzanne answered, "Sure thing, boss. I'll give Hartley's office a call." She grabbed a Granny Smith apple and a bottle of mineral water and waltzed off to her desk.

When Suzanne had started with the company, she had been overweight and depressed. But because Cora Construction provided its staff with free gym memberships as long as they used them at least twice a week, Suzanne had started working out. Then, encouraged by the corporate culture to embrace new eating habits, she'd started to pay attention to her diet—in a constructive way, rather than through the kind of yo-yo fad diets that had never worked for her. Within eight months, Suzanne had lost fifty pounds and effectively turned her life around.

Later that afternoon, Mike reached Hartley on the phone, and they went over the numbers for the Dallas interchange. Hartley reiterated how much money Cora Construction had been saving on its health insurance since it had instituted a corporate wellness plan five years ago.

As Mike had suspected, the problems with the joint bid on Dallas appeared to lie in Walt's camp. Walt's per-person healthcare costs were significantly higher than Mike's. But Mike was also aware that the problem was actually in Walt's *total* cost of healthcare, a concept about which Hartley had repeatedly educated him. Mike knew that proactive healthcare-plan risk management not only reduces healthcare costs but also reduces absenteeism, presenteeism, disability insurance, and workers' compensation insurance costs, while at the same time increasing employee productivity. Over the six-year estimated construction period of the Dallas interchange, these reduced costs would have saved Walt over seven million dollars! If Walt had had a proactive healthcare-plan risk-management program, their joint venture bid would have been 1 percent lower, and they would have won instead of being 1.5 percent over and losing.

Mike mapped out his strategy for announcing this news to Walt.

Chapter 8: Walt Drills Down

All the way back to Phoenix, Walt was in a bad mood. It lasted into the next day, and when he walked into his office around 10 A.M., he was wearing a big scowl. Fortunately, his assistant, Maggie, had worked with Walt for many years. She was used to his moods and wasn't intimidated by them like some of the other staff.

Maggie knew enough, however, to let her boss down a few cups of coffee before approaching him to go over things to do that day. She also knew another secret to helping Walt cheer up when he was in a foul temper like this one. She popped down to the concourse level of their building and bought a dozen doughnuts, making sure to include plenty of glazed crullers—Walt's favorite.

She held the box aloft as she came into Walt's office.

"Oh, Mags," he said, looking up from the pile of papers spread messily all over his huge desk. "You're an angel. Let me grab a few of those and then take the rest out to the staff room. We're going to have a busy day ahead, so might as well give the folks a sweet treat."

Walt helped himself to a couple of crullers, as Maggie suspected he would. She picked out one of her own favorites—double-chocolate glaze—before taking a seat in front of Walt's desk and pulling out her notepad.

"So, as you heard, Mags, we got slaughtered on the bid for the Dallas interchange," Walt began. "We're losing these things a lot more than we used to. And a lot more than I'm comfortable with. We need to drill down and see what in the world went wrong on this one. So you'll need to get the executive team together at noon on the dot, and we'll start going through the files."

Maggie made some notes and then gathered her things to leave. Walt glanced up from his notes and added, "You might as well order us some pizza for the lunch, Maggie. It's going be stressful enough working through this."

Chapter 9: What Walt Discovers

By noon, the three key executives at Midland Building Associates were gathered around the conference table in the corporate boardroom. They included Joe Burtinski, the chief financial officer. Like Walt, his roots were in the Midwest, though his parents had immigrated to the United States from Poland. Heddy Flanagan was the human resources manager at Midland. She was in her late forties and had been with Walt for a number of years. The newest member of the team was Maria Carrera, the risk manager. She was in her mid thirties and full of spunk and initiative.

The executives had heard about the disappointing results in Austin. As they got ready to go into the meeting, they stopped by the office kitchen to get some snacks, a common practice at Midland. There was a lot to choose from. Large vending machines displayed a wide array of chips and candy. The fridge was full of soft drinks, nestled in among some leftover pizza. And cakes and cookies, which a couple of staffers had brought in, sat on the counter.

Even the fresh-baked goods weren't enough to cheer people up, and the mood in the boardroom was subdued as Walt went through a blow-by-blow account of what had happened. He wrapped up his talk by saying, "We got royally whupped. And not for the first time. I don't want this to happen again. It's bad for the ego, to say nothing of the bottom line. Now is there any way on earth that we could have come up with lower numbers on our end?"

Joe was the first to speak up. "We knew we were a little high on some of the line items, but we thought the overall bid was competitive. The problem is, our bidding process is being impacted by the need to offset our rising healthcare costs—they're spiraling through the roof."

"Oh, God. Healthcare," Walt rolled his eyes. He liked to deal with the nuts and bolts of the construction business, not the fine print. Insurance was one thing that made his eyes glaze over.

Heddy was well aware of that but knew that she had to jump in.

"We just got hit with an 18 percent increase in our healthcare insurance," she said.

"Eighteen bloody percent?" Walt exploded.

"Harry van Parks, our insurance broker, says it's unavoidable," Heddy replied.

"Well, what about cost-shifting?" Walt asked in exasperation. "Can't we cut some benefits or something?"

Everyone in the room tensed up because they knew this was part of a running battle between Walt and Heddy.

"Walter," she started. "Our staff is already stretched to the max. Morale is down; absenteeism is up. If we cut benefits or raised premiums, we'd have a revolution on our hands. And we need every single worker on board to supply manpower for future projects. Staff turnover is so high and so many people are off on extended sick leave that this is becoming a real concern."

"Oh, Heddy," Walt sighed. "You've got a point, of course. But isn't there anything we can do about those bloody premiums?"

Joe piped in, "Harry's doing his best, Walt, he really is. He's promised to shop around for a new provider who could get us a better rate."

During the meeting, they looked at their healthcare costs and determined that they were in fact $1,834 higher per person than Cora's costs. But that still wasn't enough to bridge the $4.5 million gap by which they had lost the bid.

Walt still had no idea he had a problem . . . until he met again with Mike.

Chapter 10: What the Heck Is That?

A week later, Walt had to pass through Austin on some other business, and he arranged to meet up with Mike to go over the numbers from their failed bid. It wasn't the first time Walt had been in Mike's office, but he was always a bit surprised. Staff were always coming and going with gym bags and tennis rackets. The sound of blenders echoed through the hallway from the office kitchen, and people were always carrying out their containers of smoothies or handfuls of fresh fruit.

The first person Walt saw today as he came into the lobby was Suzanne. She waved him down the hall to Mike's office. Walt strode in with his usual big steps and gave Mike a strong pat on the back.

"Looks like you're running some kind of spa here," he joked. He pointed at the small device, a bit like a miniature pager, that Mike was wearing on his belt. Walt had noticed other people around the office wearing one too.

"Isn't that one of those thingies that measures how far you walk or something like that?" Walt asked.

"Sort of," Mike replied. "It's called a KAM—a kinetic activity monitor. It shows how much physical activity you're getting during the day—the intensity of everything you do on your feet. And you use it to keep track of how many servings of fruits and vegetables you're eating."

"You don't say," Walt said with a shrug. He was used to Mike being a fitness nut, but he wanted to get down to business. So he quickly pulled some papers out of his briefcase and started talking numbers.

"Well, we've done the drill-down," Walt said. "I've gone through the figures inside out, up and down, front and back. But there's no way we could have come up with a lower number for the Dallas project. The only significant difference in our numbers is healthcare, $1.8 million over six years. That's not enough to change the outcome."

Mike pulled out his papers too. "Actually, we're quite in the opposite situation, Walt. Insurance costs are where we've been saving most of our money. Last year alone, our cost trend was 12 percent below the national average, which adds up to about $600,000. You're right that your healthcare costs were $1.8 million higher. But do you know what your total cost of healthcare is?"

Walt shook his head.

"For every dollar that is spent on direct medical and pharmacy costs, there is more than three dollars spent on health-related productivity costs," Mike explained. "These are things like absenteeism. Or presenteeism, when an employee comes to work but isn't productive on the job because of health-related issues. Those productivity costs include things like overtime and turnover, customer dissatisfaction, and inconsistent product quality."

Walt's jaw dropped. "Why is Mike Lopez beating me at a business I think I know so well?" he wondered.

Despite his overwhelmingly self-confident demeanor, Walt was a smart enough businessman to admit what he didn't know. So he said to Mike, matter-of-factly, "Our companies look alike on paper. My people look like your people. So how come you're killing me in competition?"

"Actually, I've been there myself, Walt," Mike replied. "Six years ago, I found we weren't being nearly as productive as we could be. I kept telling myself there had to be a better way of doing business. Then, as luck would have it, I was looking for a tennis partner for a game at my health club one afternoon. I ended up playing with a guy called Hartley. Of course, between shots, we got to talking about our jobs. Turns out Hartley worked with healthcare insurance, but in a completely different way from the traditional brokers that you and I are used to. We spoke a lot about this, both during the game and afterward. And within short order, Hartley became Cora's healthcare-plan risk-management consultant."

"Your what-consultant?" Walt interjected. "What the heck is that?"

"I know, I know," Mike said. "I was just like you. I didn't know someone like him existed. Hartley is a hybrid of so many things. The first thing he said to me after our game was, 'I'm going to show you a new way of looking at things.'

"I was skeptical, to tell you the honest truth, and I went away to think about it," Mike continued. "I talked to my existing broker about some of the ideas that Hartley had mentioned, and my broker thought it was a waste of time."

Walt laughed. "Hoo boy. I bet. That's exactly what ol' Harry van Parks, my broker, would say too. I can just hear him."

"But the reason I was interested," Mike continued, "was because of how sure Hartley was of his approach. He was so sure that he said he would work for a small base fee plus a percentage of the company's savings, rather than a standard commission on premiums. I figured that was the biggest testament I could hear. So I decided to try it. And I have to tell you, Walt, there's been no looking back.

"Hartley handles so many things for us: insurance benefits, drug plans, physician networks. And he assembled all these proactive strategies to lower healthcare costs. Hartley convinced me that skyrocketing healthcare costs are an opportunity for those who proactively manage their healthcare risk."

"Well, Mikey," Walt finally said after a long moment of reflection. "I can't say I'm not skeptical. But I've got nothing to lose. Can you give me the number for this Hartley fellow, the genius guy, and we'll see what he can do for us?"

Mike was happy to oblige. As they ended the meeting, Mike gave Walt one more piece of advice. "You know, Walt, for this to work, you really need to believe that change is possible because, as Henry Ford said, 'Whether you think you can or can't, you're right.'"

PART II

——

A NEW WAY OF
DOING THINGS

Chapter 11: Who Is Hartley?

Hartley Smith was a healthcare-plan risk-management consultant; that meant he was an insurance broker—but an insurance broker with a difference. Through his company, Principal Risk Management, he sold healthcare insurance to corporate clients and offered them a whole range of related services.

But Hartley didn't sell healthcare insurance in the traditional way. He didn't earn his living based on a percentage of premium costs, as traditional brokers did. Hartley earned his living based on how much money he saved for his clients. His focus was really on two things: The first was to improve a company's profit margin by cutting the cost of its healthcare insurance. The second but equally important thing was to maximize the well-being of all the workers throughout the company by giving them the tools and incentives to lead healthier lives.

Hartley was thirty-nine years old and struck a memorable first impression with his six-foot-three build, red hair, and freckles. Like Walt, he was of Irish origin, though he was born and raised in Providence, Rhode Island. His father, Paul, had been an insurance broker too, the traditional kind. Paul, who had passed away when Hartley was in his early twenties, had really wanted his only son to follow him into the family business.

But Hartley's great passion while he was growing up had been sports, especially tennis. He had dreamed of a professional career, even Wimbledon, and often traveled down to the International Tennis Hall of Fame in Newport just to be reminded of the achievements of so many of his heroes on the court. But, unfortunately, Hartley had been born with a bad knee. He'd aggravated it while playing tennis as a teenager, and doctors had told him he would have to be careful in the future not to sustain further and more significant injuries.

Hartley learned an important lesson from his misfortune: the habit of getting back up on his feet. So he couldn't be a professional tennis player, Hartley told himself. He could still pursue his love of sports. With careful attention to his knee, he was still able to play recreational tennis—although certainly not as hard as he would have had to in competition.

Hartley did end up following Paul into the insurance business. Over time, he gradually transformed his father's traditional insurance practice into a risk-management consulting business, Principal Risk Management, where he served a select group of clients located across the

United States. His transition to consulting allowed him the flexibility to choose where he lived.

He finally ended up in the Southwest, drawn there by the weather, which allowed year-round enjoyment of many outdoor recreational activities. Cycling had grown to be one of his favorite sports, and Hartley settled in Austin, loving the excellent infrastructure that made it one of the most bike-friendly cities in North America.

In fact, it was on a bike trail in Austin that Hartley met and fell in love with Tess, who was a nursing student at the time. They soon got married and bought a house. Tess worked at a retirement home until their son, Charlie, was born five years ago.

During the ten years that Principal Risk Management had been in place, it had enjoyed growing success, and Hartley had made countless presentations to CEOs about his program. So when the call came through that Walt Williams, owner of Midland Building Associates in Phoenix, wanted to meet with him, Hartley was well prepared.

He didn't have to do very much work to polish off the presentation he would make to Walt. He was passionate about this subject and knew his material inside out and backward, so Hartley simply clicked onto his travel profile on his computer and booked himself a flight from Austin to the Arizona capital in two days' time.

Chapter 12: Walt Meets Hartley

Over the next couple of days, Walt was busy with other business. When he was leaving the office after a hard day, Maggie looked up from her desk and reminded him, "Walt, you have your meeting with Hartley Smith bright and early tomorrow morning."

Walt sputtered, "Hartley who? Who the heck is that?"

Maggie answered, "It's Mike Lopez's healthcare-plan risk-management consultant, Walt. The insurance guy from Austin."

Walt sighed. "Oh yeah, him. The wellness guru. I guess it must have slipped my mind. Do you think we should have a nice big box of crullers to welcome him to Midland?"

Maggie rolled her eyes and laughed.

Walt sighed again. "Okay, okay. No more kidding around. See you tomorrow, kiddo."

The next morning, Walt kept Hartley waiting for only fifteen minutes, which was impressive for Walt when he was trying to avoid something.

Walt was used to a lot of long-winded business spiels. And his motto at work, as in life, was "What's the bottom line?" So for his first meeting with Hartley, Walt was all set to put this upstart through his paces.

As soon as Hartley sat down in the big leather armchair in Walt's large corner office, the CEO said, not in an unfriendly manner but a blunt one, "Now, I've heard some good things about you from Mike Lopez. And I have a lot of admiration for Mike. So I'm perfectly willing to let you have your say.

"But I don't have all the time in the world, and I'm sure you don't either. So I want you to cut to the chase and start with your best offer. If you only had one argument and only five minutes to win me over, what would that be? Hit me with your best shot. And how soon can you get me a quote?" At this, Walt sat back in his chair expecting the young man in front of him to look flustered and nervous.

But Hartley was neither. He was prepared and he was poised. "Actually, I don't prepare bids. I work in a different way. Let me ask you one thing, Walt: How do you currently manage your healthcare risk?"

Walt was quick with his answer. "Just like everyone else. After we receive the 10 to 20 percent increase from our insurance carrier, we shop our coverage out to see if we can get a better deal."

Hartley raised his eyebrows. "So, your 'strategy' is to react to your insurance renewal and try to put your bad risk off on another insurance company?"

"Well, what am I supposed to do? Sit back and watch our healthcare costs rise every year and do nothing about it?" Walt was beginning to wonder if meeting with Hartley had been a good idea. Maybe this guy wasn't so smart after all.

Hartley leaned forward in his chair. "Your problem goes a lot deeper than rising healthcare costs. Healthcare costs are just the tip of the iceberg." He paused to pull some charts out of his briefcase and slide them across the desk to Walt. "Did you know the United States has one of the highest rates of obesity in the developed world?" Walt took a quick glance down at his own waistline as Hartley continued. "Some studies show that as many as 70 percent of healthcare claims result from the poor lifestyle decisions that Americans make. These lifestyle decisions also affect your bottom line through increased rates of employee absenteeism and presenteeism, increased disability insurance and workers' compensation insurance costs, and decreased employee productivity and creativity."

Walt made a sweeping gesture with his hand at the papers in front of him. "This is all very interesting, but what control do I have over my employees' lifestyle decisions?"

"It's not a matter of control," answered Hartley in a calm but matter-of-fact voice. "It's a matter of means, opportunity, and support. You provide your employees with the means, opportunity, and support to improve their health, and most of them will take it."

Walt gave a hesitant nod. "So, let's lay it on the line. I know Mike said something about you only getting paid if the company saves money, but there's got to be a catch. What's this really going to cost me?"

Hartley had met many CEOs, lots of them as blunt as Walt, and he knew what the most persuasive argument of all was to these guys: the bottom line. If an idea didn't save or make them money, then they just weren't interested, no matter how many wonderful do-good, save-the-world arguments you could offer to back it up.

So Hartley explained, "Mike's right. I'm so sure of my system, Walt, that if it doesn't save you money, I simply won't get paid for my work."

"Say what?" Walt's face registered disbelief. "No payola for you? I thought you insurance guys lived and died from your commissions."

Hartley spoke simply and directly. "I'm not an insurance guy, and that was the old way of doing things, Walt. My way—the new way—is completely different. I don't work on commission. I work for a percentage of your company's savings. I do charge a small base fee to cover my operating costs, but I only profit if you profit."

Walt whistled. "Okay, Hartley, you've won more than five minutes of my time. So, what exactly is this new system all about? Go ahead and give me all the details."

So Hartley began to go through it. "If you choose to work with me, you become part of a proactive healthcare-plan risk-management solution." He continued, "As your healthcare-plan risk-management consultant, I'll negotiate and set up partnerships for you with various outside providers that will ensure top-notch services for your company and its employees. These include actuarial services, healthcare providers, and wellness providers too."

Walt's brows drew together. "What the heck's a wellness provider?"

Hartley smiled. "I was wondering if you'd heard that term before. A wellness provider offers health-risk assessments and health-management tools for employees. It tests and monitors employee wellness and provides ongoing support to assist employees in meeting their health goals. Healthier employees equal lower costs and greater productivity.

"I also save my clients money by bringing companies together that are managing the same risk. I leverage their group purchasing power through negotiating group contracts," Hartley continued.

Walt nodded. "It's making sense so far. Please, go on."

So Hartley did. "Because of the volume of our business, we're able to negotiate significant discounts for your company from third-party vendors," he said. "These discounts are far greater than if you were just going in there on your own, rather than with the combined strength of the group of like-minded companies. And I'm constantly looking for new and innovative ways to save you even more money. To give you just one example, I've recently discovered an organization that makes both routine and emergency medical house calls to member clients. It provides the highest quality care at very affordable prices while dramatically decreasing the financial cost and wasted time associated with unnecessary emergency room visits."

Hartley stopped to take a breath, and Walt jumped right in. "Whoa, whoa. It sounds great. But there's so much new stuff that you're talking about. To be quite frank with you, I'm not sure we at Midland have the specialized manpower to get into all of these newfangled programs."

"I understand your concerns, Walt," Hartley responded reassuringly. "But the beauty of my system is that you don't have to worry about overburdening your company because it's my job to coordinate the whole process for you and to be the go-between between Midland and all these third-party vendors that I've been describing."

"Now you're talking," Walt said. "You've got to understand that this is all a new language to me. And you're throwing a lot of information at me cold. I'm still not sure I get how all of this plays out in real life."

Hartley replied, "Believe me, I've heard that before. It sounds a lot more complicated than it really is. The process is broken down into seven steps. And the first step is recognizing that your healthcare liability is a risk that must be proactively managed. You can even say that you're already getting Step One done just by calling me into your office for this meeting."

Walt smiled. "Great. I like to cross things off the to-do list. What are the other steps?"

"Step Two involves collecting all of the available data that we'll use to assess your company's specific healthcare insurance needs," Hartley explained. "This includes your existing plan design, provider network, plus two years of historical claims data that we then process through our claims data analysis and predictive modeling software.

"In Step Three, we ensure that you're properly prepared to tackle the problem. A key component of Step Three is something we call a cultural audit, which is basically a survey that shows the degree to which your management and employees are ready to embrace change with regard to their health and fitness. I tell CEOs when I meet them for the first time—like I'm about to tell you now—that a key thing for success with my program is to get management buy-in throughout the company. You have to develop a culture of health and fitness and it starts with your leadership. It's not as simple as just getting an okay from the company owner."

Hartley let out a laugh here, in response to the expression of mock outrage that Walt had put on.

"Just joshing, just joshing. I do that all the time. Forgive me," Walt said. "Go on."

Hartley continued his rundown. "The cultural audit shows me where the roadblocks are within your corporate culture. And typically the roadblocks come because people are afraid of change. And that's perfectly normal. "Where you will get the most push-back is from your management team. They'll be trying to slow down the process, ignoring our requests for data, because our system represents change." Hartley paused. "Do you know what Albert Einstein said is the definition of insanity?"

Walt shook his head.

"Einstein said insanity is doing the same thing over and over and expecting different results." Hartley went on, "If you continue to manage your healthcare-plan risk in the same manner as you have in the past, then why should you expect anything but double-digit increases? Once I know where the resistance is coming from, I can meet one-on-one with each member of your top management team to respond to their particular concerns. This is all part of Step Three, and it's a pretty important step. I've learned from my experience in the business that it doesn't matter how good your new programs are. If you don't have buy-in from the management, it's not going to work.

"By this point, I will have prepared in-depth reports about your company to take into these one-on-one meetings because a lot of the resistance comes from a lack of understanding. So I'll sit down with them and go over the financial data. I'll share success stories from other companies. It all takes about thirty days.

"Then we're ready for what I call the Big Meeting, where we meet with all the top managers who are now on board. And that takes care of Step Three," Hartley said.

Walt sighed. "We're only at Step Three? I thought we were at Step Thirty-Three by now."

Hartley laughed. "Don't worry, Walt, the first three steps are the hardest ones. They involve coming face-to-face with a new way of doing things. The last four stages are the nuts and bolts."

Walt nodded with enthusiasm. "Hey, that's what I like to hear—construction lingo. Run through them quick, and then I'll take you out for lunch. All this talk is making me hungry."

So Hartley explained, "Step Four involves appointing one person to be responsible for managing your healthcare-plan risk. Step Five is building the new partnerships with the third-party vendors. Step Six is rolling out the new programs to the employees. The wellness program is a great one, but it's usually voluntary in the first year, so you have to convince employees that it's worth their while to sign up. And the final step is the maintenance one, of keeping all the new programs up-to-date and running smoothly."

Walt was feeling a lot more impressed than he had initially imagined. But still, it was a lot of information to process in one sitting. He told Hartley he needed a few days to think over all of this.

Then he took Hartley out to lunch at the steakhouse just around the corner from the Midland headquarters.

Chapter 13: Discovering the Pyramid

Walt had a lot of other, unrelated matters to take care of once his meeting with Hartley was over. For the rest of the day and most of the evening, he didn't give any more thought to the idea of corporate wellness and proactive healthcare-plan risk management.

He got home around 6 P.M. When his wife, Louise, saw how tired he looked, she told him to put his feet up and relax while she finished getting dinner ready. Walt wasn't going to argue with that. He grabbed the remote to switch on the TV and went over to the bar to fix a couple of aperitifs: for Louise, a vermouth and soda, and for himself a gin martini—very dry—with a couple of olives. As he mixed these, he shook his head and wondered why most bartenders put way too much vermouth in martinis. Now, Xavier at the Blue Moon in Austin—there was a guy who knew how to make a good martini. But the thought of the Blue Moon Hotel just brought back bad memories of how he and Mike Lopez had lost that bid in

Austin, and Walt wanted to put that out of his mind for now and unwind. Walt loved to win and hated to lose. That's what made him such a great contractor.

He brought Louise her drink in the kitchen and gave it to her with a big kiss. If only the corporate world ran as smoothly as his marriage. Then Walt went back to the living room and flopped down on his favorite leather recliner to let a little bit of mindless TV settle him.

Knowing how stressed Walt was at work these days, Louise had fixed him one of his favorite meals: Caesar salad with tons of bacon bits and croutons, followed by fettuccine Alfredo. And homemade cheesy garlic bread, with a mayonnaise sauce for dipping, just the way Walt liked it. And for dessert, Louise had made her specialty, pecan pie. Walt loved it so much he could never resist seconds, with plenty of vanilla bean ice cream on the side.

After dinner, Louise left to visit her mother, who lived on her own in a condo close by, so Walt had a few hours to himself. He tried channel surfing some more, but nothing really caught his attention. And anyway, he wasn't really focusing on the programs. His mind kept on wandering off to the things he had spoken about with Hartley earlier that day.

That's when the fierce competitor in Walt kicked in. He was tired of losing bids. He took any advantage that he could get, and he now was convinced that he could gain a significant competitive edge by proactively managing Midland's healthcare-plan risk.

Walt decided to spend some time on the Internet to see what more he could find out about corporate wellness. He wandered over to the den and sat down in front of the computer. But even before turning it on, he had to take a second to loosen his belt a few notches. "Perhaps I shouldn't have had seconds at dinner," he thought to himself in an uncharacteristic moment of sheepishness.

With the help of Google and a few key search words such as "obesity," "diabetes," "nutrition," and "cholesterol," Walt had no trouble turning up a large amount of material to go through. He shook his head with disbelief as he read through some of the statistics. And he asked himself how he could have missed this health epidemic that was developing in the United States. He found himself agreeing with much of what Hartley had told him. None of this could be good for employee morale or their job performance. And, in consequence, it was only logical that it couldn't be any good at all for the bottom line.

The next site that Walt got through as he was going down the list was called My Pyramid. Clicking it open, he noticed it was run by the Center for Nutritional Policy and Promotion of the US Department of Agriculture. Its mission was to promote the optimal nutritional standards of the so-called food pyramid. Walt found some interactive tools there that allowed users to keep track of their diet and exercise on a day-to-day basis. This was not something he had ever thought about doing. But then again, Walt was finding himself thinking about a lot of new things these days. "Why not?" he decided. He'd give it a shot.

First of all, he had to create a user profile with his age, gender, height, and weight. Walt was five foot ten—that part was easy—but he had no idea how much he weighed, although he reluctantly admitted to himself that his clothes had been feeling tighter and tighter these days. Walt knew Louise had a scale somewhere in the house. So, with a sigh, he got up from the desk to track it down.

What Walt saw when he looked down at the digital number gave him a jolt: 240 pounds. He had put on twenty-five pounds from what he remembered weighing a couple of years ago at his last medical appointment. And that was sixty pounds more than what he considered his fighting weight.

Walt swallowed hard. Where had all those extra pounds come from?

With renewed interest, he went back to his computer and began to calculate a nutritional analysis of what he had eaten that day. He had to make a list of everything—everything!—he had eaten that day and in what quantity.

Walt had had eggs Benedict at his favorite diner that morning since he'd been running late for work. Then, at lunch, when he took Hartley out to the steakhouse, he had ordered one of its amazing all-dressed burgers with fries. There was a candy bar from the vending machine in the office kitchen in the middle of the afternoon, when he'd been feeling sluggish. And he'd helped himself to a piece of leftover cake that one of his staff had brought in. Plus the feast that Louise had prepared for him tonight. Coffee with cream and sugar during the day. A couple of martinis and almost a full bottle of red wine with dinner.

In the time that it took for the computer program to calculate the total number of calories Walt had consumed that day, he admitted to himself that the results wouldn't be pretty. And they weren't. Walt's total calorie intake was more than triple what was recommended for his age and size. And, naturally, he hadn't had any exercise that day, which would have burned some of these calories. Walt had had no idea that the piece of cake that he'd eaten as a snack represented 20 percent of his ideal caloric intake.

That clinched it for Walt: Midland Building Associates was going to join up with Hartley's program at Principal Risk Management and institute a corporate wellness program. It was decided in Walt's mind, and not a moment too soon, he told himself—for both his company's well-being and his own personal health.

Though it had been a shocking realization, Walt found himself feeling pretty good as he was getting ready for bed—not good about the weight he'd put on, of course, nor about Midland's current financial problems. But he was feeling optimistic that he had found a way of dealing with the issues, a way that made sense to him and made him feel in control again.

Chapter 14: Spicing Up the Lunch Order

Walt had a lot to sleep on that night: what he'd learned from Hartley and what he'd learned on his own. He woke up the next morning feeling invigorated. It had been a few weeks since he'd gotten ready for work with such energy. Losing the bid on the Dallas interchange had been bringing Walt down more than he had cared to admit, even to himself.

But this morning, Walt was whistling as he made his way into the office.

Maggie looked up with surprise. It had been a while since she'd seen her boss looking so cheery.

"Good morning, Maggie," Walt sang out. "Beautiful day, isn't it?"

Maggie glanced out the window at the gray sky that threatened rain but didn't say anything.

Walt, however, was feeling the kind of adrenaline that made him notice all the little things around him. He had seen her look outside and felt a bad pun brewing.

"Nah, it's too lame," he told himself. And then a second later, he figured, "What the heck. Go for it."

So Walt said to his assistant, "Maggie, my dear. They're just a few little clouds. I'm not going to let that . . . *dampen* . . . my enthusiasm."

Maggie laughed despite herself. It was a good sign when Walt started to throw bad puns around.

"So, Maggie, it's going to be a busy day." Walt started going through his to-do list.

"I'd like you to organize a lunch meeting for the key management team for tomorrow, please. Tell them attendance is imperative. Have lots of pads and pens on hand, and at least three flip charts. We have a lot of information to go over."

"Sure thing, Walt," Maggie replied. She reached down into her drawer to show him some takeout menus from the neighborhood restaurants from which they usually ordered lunch for staff meetings. They'd had pizza last time; maybe they'd want Chinese tomorrow, she told herself.

"And for lunch . . ." Walt interrupted her train of thought, "I'd like . . ." he paused here for effect, enjoying his anticipation of Maggie's reaction in the next split second.

"I'd like . . . fresh fruit, grilled chicken breasts, lots of fresh vegetables—carrots, cucumbers, broccoli—and some dip."

Walt was walking away from Maggie's desk toward his office, when he turned around and added, "Low-fat dip, of course."

"Of course," Maggie said with a chuckle. With Walt, you never knew what cards he was keeping up his sleeve.

Chapter 15: A Big Announcement

The next day, about ten minutes before noon, Walt made a point of getting to the boardroom before any of the team had arrived. He usually tried to be the last one to walk into a meeting—it was just an instinctive feeling he had that a CEO should be the one who kept people waiting rather than vice versa. But today Walt wanted to be sure to see his managers' reactions when they walked in and saw the healthy lunch spread that was laid out on the credenza along the side of the room, rather than the usual fast-food fare.

Joe was the first one to arrive.

"Ah, Walt. I could eat a horse," Joe said as he rambled into the room. "What's on the menu today? Don't know about you, but I'm having a hankering for a little fried chicken."

He obviously hadn't noticed the food yet.

"Well, we're having chicken, all right," Walt chuckled.

When Joe looked over at the platters of carrot sticks and broccoli florets, he stopped in his tracks and did an imitation of a cowboy reining in his horse. "Whoa, boy," he sputtered. "Is this Weight Watchers or something?"

"Well, I was just getting a bit tired of the same old routine," Walt responded with nonchalance.

Maria arrived and had a similar reaction to Joe's. But Walt just smiled like a Cheshire cat. He bit into a carrot stick and motioned for her to fill up her plate, as well.

A few minutes later, when they had settled back into their seats, Walt looked at his watch and noted that Heddy was still missing.

Suddenly, a flustered Heddy burst in through the closed door. She looked preoccupied and didn't even notice, as the others had, the very different kind of lunch laid out in the room.

Walt could sense that something was bugging Heddy and that he'd have to talk to her one-on-one after the meeting to see what was up. But he didn't have time to worry about it now. He had an important announcement to make to his key staff. So he launched right into it.

"As you're all aware, we've run into some difficulties lately. We want to put these behind us as quickly as possible and get back on a winning track," Walt explained. Heads nodded around the table.

"Certain costs are skyrocketing. Like health insurance, for instance," Walt went on. Heddy's nodding got even more vehement here.

"Now, I know that I usually leave these kinds of matters up to some of you to look after, but I decided it was about time that I got up to speed on some of this stuff myself," Walt said. "So I started to ask around and talk to some folks and even do some research." He smiled because he knew it was a running joke around the office that he hated background research as much as he loved hands-on nuts and bolts stuff.

"And in the course of this research, I came across an interesting idea that I hadn't heard of before . . . something called proactive healthcare-plan risk management."

Walt continued. "I've been dealing with Hartley Smith, a healthcare-plan risk-management consultant who has a company called Principal Risk Management. Now, Hartley's got this innovative program for saving us a ton of money while at the same time making all of us at the company—and that includes me—a heck of a lot healthier and more productive."

He noted the puzzled faces around him and went on to explain, in more or less Hartley's words, the conversation he'd had with the healthcare-plan risk-management consultant. He began to go through the seven steps, even getting out of his chair to write them down on a flip chart as he spoke. Joe and Heddy exchanged glances. This was very unusual behavior for Walt.

Silence greeted the end of Walt's presentation. But it was only for a moment. Then everyone started asking questions.

"Will we need to switch doctor networks?" Maria looked worried. "I really like the doctor I have now. If we switch, she might not be in the network."

Walt nodded. Hartley had mentioned that this was one of many common concerns. "Yes, Hartley has indicated that we may indeed need to switch networks, but he also informed me that most of the national carriers have excellent coverage in our area." He smiled at Maria and continued, "And as managers of the company, our job is to do what is in the best interest of the company and of the employees who count on us to make good decisions, not just of ourselves."

Joe jumped in. "But, Walt, our increases have been keeping pace with national averages. What's the problem?"

"Come on, Joe," Walt replied, "since when has being average been one of our goals? We're not going to win contracts by being average."

Walt sat down and addressed his team. "You know, Hartley told me that Einstein's definition of insanity is doing the same thing over and over again and expecting a different result. And, boy, did that ever hit home. If we keep managing our healthcare-plan risk the same as we have in the past, then why should we expect anything other than double-digit increases?"

Heddy shook her head. "I don't know, Walt. This is going to be a hard sell. The employees really don't like change."

Walt smiled at Heddy. As much as he respected her, he sensed the truth behind her comment. "No offense, Heddy, but do you mean the employees don't like change or that you don't like dealing with change? Individual employees are really going to benefit from this, not just the company. Our job is to help them understand the benefits and make their transition as easy as possible."

"I hear what you're saying, Walt, but there's a lot going on right now, and we all have a lot on our plates. Do we really have time to make this kind of change? Maybe this is something we should put off until next year." Joe looked around the table as he finished speaking, and the others nodded their agreement.

Walt paused briefly before replying. "Hey, I know we're all busy, but we don't have time not to change. We are losing contracts to more competitive contractors, and if we don't manage this risk, then we'll be out of business in ten years."

Walt gave them a moment to let this sink in, then said, "Well, folks, I appreciate the kinds of questions you've raised, but I agree with Hartley. Like him, I've come to the realization that rising healthcare costs are an opportunity to gain a competitive advantage. And that's exactly what I want Midland to have.

"Now, over the next couple of weeks, Hartley is going to administer a survey throughout the company—the cultural audit he calls it. As management, you'll have to fill out two surveys. The first one concerns your views

about how open Midland is to corporate change. The
second one is for every single person at Midland, including me, about how healthy our current lifestyles are and
how much we want to improve. Now, I know that
a lot of you might be thinking, 'What's Walt Williams
doing spouting his mouth off about healthy lifestyles?'
And I'm the first to admit that I have to make changes,
and this kind of lunch spread that we've had here today
is just an example."

Walt started to organize his papers to wrap up the
meeting. "Thanks for your time, everyone," he said.
"Hartley will be meeting with each one of you one-on-
one after he has the results of the cultural audit. And I
expect all of you to give him your full cooperation."

Chapter 16: Meeting Joe

Joe Burtinski had a great sense of humor, something he shared with his boss. He and Walt were always trying to outdo each other with bad puns and practical jokes. But the other side of Joe was that, at the age of forty-four, he was a passionate and accomplished CFO with a brilliant mind for numbers and a great ability to look forward and plan the growth of the company.

After reviewing the results of the cultural audit, Hartley was well aware of what kind of information would work to convince Joe of the merits of his plan. So Hartley came amply prepared for his one-on-one meeting at Joe's office. He brought in stacks of charts, data printouts, and spreadsheets.

Hartley began by asking, "So, Joe, tell me, what are your feelings about Midland proactively managing its healthcare-plan risk?"

"Well, in principle, I like the idea of being proactive," Joe said. "But I'm not 100 percent convinced. I mean, maybe wellness is just a feel-good term."

"That's an excellent point, Joe," Hartley replied. He was unfazed by the kinds of reservations that Joe was expressing. After all, he had heard a lot worse.

"Of course, it's always somewhat destabilizing when you're doing something new," Hartley continued, "but I've got some specific examples that might paint the picture more clearly."

"Oh, good, nuts and bolts," Joe said with a grin, and Hartley smiled too. One of his great strengths in business was that he paid a lot of attention to the kinds of little things that less observant people would miss, like catch phrases and personality traits. So, in his short time dealing with Midland, he'd already learned that "nuts and bolts" was one of Walt's favorite expressions.

So Hartley asked Joe, "Do you know what the total cost of your healthcare is per employee?"

"Well, it's about $5,000 a year for medical and pharmacy costs," Joe answered.

Hartley asked, "And what about health-related productivity costs that come from absenteeism and presenteeism? Things like customer dissatisfaction and uneven product quality. Did you know that this costs over $15,000 a year per employee?"

Joe whistled in amazement. "That could go a long way to explaining why we lost the Dallas job," he said.

"Let me show you the kinds of reports we provide our clients," Hartley said. "Keep in mind that these are actual costs incurred, not what the employees self-report.

So they're a lot more accurate in terms of telling us what's really going on with your company's healthcare costs."

Hartley ruffled through a stack of spreadsheets, running down the line items with his pen. "Ah, here, here's a good example," he said. "Look at this cluster of costs around emergency-room visits. Now, that might seem to you to just be one of those costs that you can't do much about. After all, an emergency is an emergency, right?"

Joe nodded patiently.

"Now, part of my job," Hartley continued, "is to always be checking through these kinds of statistics. And I continuously go back to clients with my findings—not just to confirm bad news about cost increases. I'm constantly brainstorming and going back to them with solutions on cutting costs and improving the overall health and productivity of their workforce. I'm always looking at the financial impact."

Joe smiled. He liked that kind of language. He nodded at Hartley to go on with his example.

So Hartley continued. "Now if you stop to think of why so many employees of construction companies are going to emergency rooms, you might think it's because this is a very physically demanding line of work, and despite excellent safety programs, accidents still do happen.

"But there's another reason," Hartley said, "and that has to do with the fact that this business involves so much geographic mobility. Employees often end up working on projects far away from their homes and far from their regular family physicians. And in this kind of situation, they might end up going to an emergency room because it's the only place they know of in a new town where they can get treatment for a common ailment like a bad cough or the flu.

"Now, if these guys only knew the names and locations of drop-in urgent-care facilities in the new community where they're working temporarily, then they could go there instead of to emergency rooms . . ."

". . . and save a heck of a lot of money!" Joe jumped in and finished Hartley's thought.

Hartley said, "Bingo! So what I've done in this case is to set up a system whereby my clients automatically have access to a list of addresses and phone numbers for urgent-care facilities whenever they have a work crew going out of town."

"And so these are the kinds of cost-saving measures that you're giving your clients?" Joe asked.

"This is just one example of many, Joe," Hartley replied. "And this is just one small idea . . . the tip of the iceberg."

Joe was smiling. Despite his initial reluctance, he was beginning to see the benefits of joining up with a guy like Hartley.

Chapter 17: Meeting Maria

Maria Carrera was in her mid-thirties and already had an enviable reputation as one of the most forward-thinking risk managers in the country. She had been recruited to Midland three years ago. And in her short time at the company, the safety programs she had instituted had already won several prestigious national awards.

But other than her professional qualifications, Maria also had a great personality: easygoing, flexible, open to suggestions. This made her a favorite among employees and management alike. Although she was kept extremely busy with her numerous responsibilities, she always had time to talk to people and to listen to their ideas. She liked to brainstorm and asked a lot of questions.

Maria had been born in Mexico and her family had come to the United States when she was a young girl. But she still spoke fluent Spanish, which was a great advantage in her job since she dealt with many workers for whom it was also their first language. Since she was currently single, Maria spent a lot of her personal time volunteering. She was one of the founders of a charity in Phoenix that helped recent legal Hispanic immigrants access social services.

Maria's other great passion in life was sports. She had been a track star in high school and had recently started to train for her first ever triathlon.

Based on her survey results, Hartley was pretty confident that he could count on Maria's support for the new model he was proposing for Midland's healthcare-plan risk management.

Maria's office was small but brightly decorated. All over the walls, pinned up in neat order, were a variety of posters promoting safety on job sites. These were all projects started since she'd taken over as risk manager. A table beside her desk was stacked high with pamphlets, CDs, and DVDs, all of them also related to safety initiatives. Her office didn't feel messy or chaotic. It simply came across as a place full of tantalizing information, a lot like a public library.

Maria waved Hartley in with one of the big smiles that were her trademark at Midland. "Oh, excuse the lack of space," she said. "We just have so many safety programs on the go that a lot of the extra material ends up in here."

"No worries," Hartley said. "It looks like there's a ton of great stuff."

"Yup, they sure do keep me busy," she said.

"So, Maria," Hartley ventured, "have you had a chance to think about what Walt proposed in terms of updating how Midland handles its health insurance?"

"Oh my, yes," Maria said. "I've been thinking about it nonstop since I first heard about it. It's such a fabulous plan that I wonder why nobody put it all together before you. Why, just the other day, I was telling myself that something needs to be done about educating employees about healthcare in much the same way that we do about safety. You seem to have so many good initiatives already in place. Tell me about some of them."

"I'd love to," Hartley responded with enthusiasm. "The cornerstone of our process is building a corporate culture to promote health and fitness among employees. We've seen such fantastic results in people working with wellness advocates. In one instance, fifty employees dropped a total of over 400 pounds in only six months. We've helped people quit smoking, gotten them off medications, like high-blood-pressure pills, simply by encouraging them to exercise and eat healthily. It often starts with little things, like getting rid of vending machines filled with junk and having good, healthy food available in workplace kitchens instead."

Maria nodded. "You're absolutely right. I'm doing a lot of studying about nutrition, and eating the right foods really does sustain energy and increase productivity. We have recently contracted with a new mobile food vending service. Their vending trucks carry only healthy and nutritious food, and their drivers have been specially trained in construction safety. They can only park in designated areas. No more driving on half-finished bridges or other unsafe places. Instead of delivering junk food in hazardous conditions, they now deliver nutritious food in a safe environment."

Hartley nodded enthusiastically.

"How do you get the message out to people about the wellness programs?" Maria asked.

"Well, we use a lot of the same methods that you do for your safety programs," Hartley said. "Paycheck stuffers, posters, DVDs. And we're also reaching out to workers whose first language isn't English. All of our material is available in Spanish. And there are Spanish-speaking wellness advocates too."

"You read my mind and my next question," Maria said. "And I have another question."

"By all means," Hartley said.

"Well, as you might guess, in our business, the workplace tends to be very spread out, with dozens of job sites in dozens of locations. How do programs like these work for that situation?"

Hartley was really enjoying this conversation. "That's an excellent question," he said. "A lot of support services—like the wellness telephone advocates—have extended hours. And we really want to reach not only employees but their families too because that's where so many decisions that affect healthcare are made. So spouses of staff can also participate in the wellness programs. And we've had great success piggybacking wellness initiatives on other existing programs . . ."

". . . like the safety programs!" Maria finished his thought with a big smile. "Yes, that's fabulous. I mean, at Midland, we have five-minute safety meetings at the start of every workday, and longer ones every Friday. We use that time to discuss safety issues and initiatives. We could just . . ."

". . . piggyback information on health and wellness at the safety meetings." This time it was Hartley who jumped in and finished Maria's thoughts.

They both started laughing.

"But seriously," Hartley continued. "All of these measures that we've just talked about are great and very effective. But the one thing that is key—without which none of this can work—is support and energy from the company's upper management. That is absolutely essential to the success of the program."

"Well, one thing's for sure," said Maria. "You've got my support, and I'll do everything I can to get the message out to my colleagues."

Chapter 18: Meeting Heddy

At age forty-seven, Heddy Flanagan had worked in human resources for the past ten years. It was a second career for her. She'd had a very successful stint running a day care out of her home when her son, Tom, was little. Heddy was the classic example of a people person: kind, compassionate, and caring. Parents who had entrusted their young ones to Heddy's care thought the world of her because she would always go the extra mile, putting in extra hours with nary a word of complaint if somebody was sick or running late.

When Tom started school full time, Heddy went back to college and earned a diploma in human resources. She got top-notch grades, excelled at her job placements, and had no trouble finding work once she graduated.

Midland was the second company at which she had been an HR manager. Until five years before, she'd held a similar position in a food-processing company in El Paso, Texas. But her family had decided to relocate to Phoenix, and that was when she started at Midland.

There were several reasons for the Flanagans' move to Arizona. Heddy's seventy-six-year-old mother, Anna, lived in Phoenix. Anna was plagued by a growing number of health problems, including diabetes, and she was finding it harder and harder to live on her own in the big family house where she and her late husband had raised their five children.

And Heddy's husband, Victor, was off work on extended sick leave. He was a highly respected construction foreman, but he had had to go in for triple bypass surgery in their last year in El Paso. The recovery time was long and depressing for Victor. When he did go back to work after the surgery, he wasn't feeling sure on his feet and within a month had thrown out his back so badly that the doctors weren't optimistic about whether he could ever return to the job that he loved. With Victor's health problems, the family income was decreased dramatically. So when some of Victor's colleagues told the Flanagans that Midland was looking for a new HR manager, Heddy applied for the job and ended up getting it. And that was how the family ended up in Phoenix, living with Heddy's mother.

Between taking care of Victor and Anna and raising Tom, who was now seventeen and having some trouble at school, Heddy had a full plate of domestic concerns. But she tried her hardest not to let this affect the time or the effort she devoted to her job at Midland. She was always giving 100 percent. Heddy felt a tremendous amount of empathy for Midland employees, especially the guys who worked on the construction crews. By the same token, she also knew how vocal they could be when someone rocked their boat, and she worked hard to keep them happy.

Heddy was ultrasensitive and highly protective of the benefits program she administered at Midland. And whenever Walt or Joe spoke of money matters, soaring healthcare costs, and the need to cut back on benefits, Heddy rose passionately to defend the status quo. She certainly didn't need anyone to come in and tell her how to do her job, upset the employees, and heap more work on her already overburdened back. "Leave well enough alone" was Heddy's favorite catchphrase.

So all things considered, it was not surprising that Heddy had huge reservations about Hartley and the new healthcare insurance system he was proposing for Midland. It was clear that she saw him as an upstart who had no right barging in on the company and distracting it from far more pressing matters.

Hartley was smart and perceptive enough to have sensed this from the beginning, putting two and two together after Walt had gone through the rundown of his top managers. Heddy had already rescheduled the one-on-one meeting with Hartley three times. Her survey results had only served to reinforce Hartley's awareness of Heddy's resistance to what he was proposing.

Hartley arrived outside Heddy's office and knocked respectfully on her half-open door. She waved him in.

"I'm very sorry for all the delays, Mr. Smith," she began.

"Hartley. Please call me Hartley," he told her.

"Yeah, okay." She nodded distractedly. "As I was saying, Hartley, it's an incredibly busy time for us right now. I'm renegotiating benefits packages. Morale is way down. We've got a ton of people off on sick leave. Absenteeism is really a problem. . . ."

She seemed ready to go on down the list in great detail when Hartley delicately cut her off. "Heddy—may I call you Heddy?" Heddy nodded her consent. "Heddy, I couldn't agree with you more." Heddy looked suspicious. This was obviously some trick.

Hartley continued. "Staff morale is extremely important to the success of the company, and the health and well-being of Midland's employees is really what I want to talk to you about. I know that what Walt and I are proposing may sound like a lot of needless extra work to you, not to mention the push-back you're probably anticipating from the employees, am I right?" Heddy frowned but gave a quick nod of begrudging agreement.

"Believe me when I say that this change is going to result not just in a company that is more competitive, but also in employees who are much happier and healthier." Heddy still looked doubtful. Hartley pressed on. "My firm has dealt with exactly this situation literally hundreds of times, and I assure you that we have the necessary systems and procedures in place to assist you in helping the Midland employees through this transition."

Suddenly the cell phone on the desk in front of Heddy started to vibrate loudly. She glanced down at the call display with a worried look.

"I'm sorry," she muttered, "but I really have to take this."

As Heddy flipped open the handset, Hartley started to get out of his chair to give her some privacy. But she motioned distractedly at him to stay seated.

The worry lines etched onto Heddy's face got more and more pronounced as she listened to what the caller was telling her. A young man's animated voice on the other end of the receiver was audible.

"Tom, honey, is Mom all right? Is she conscious? Did you call an ambulance? Just stay calm. They'll be there any second. And I'm coming home this very minute."

As Heddy snapped her phone shut, she was already halfway out of her chair and reaching down for her bag under the desk.

Before Hartley could even open his mouth to ask if everything was okay, she said in a shaky voice, "I have to go. Right away. There's been an emergency. My mother's in diabetic shock."

Chapter 19: A Progress Update

After Heddy's panicked departure from their meeting, Hartley had about an hour to kill before his last appointment of the day. He was scheduled to give Walt an update of how his one-on-one interviews with Midland's executive team had gone that week.

Heddy's reaction had not been entirely unexpected. But having just witnessed all the color drain out of her face when she got that emergency call, Hartley was feeling pretty shaken up himself. He hoped everything was going to be okay with her mother. He knew what it was like to worry about the health of aging parents.

Hartley felt a knot of tension throbbing in his right shoulder. He had to unwind a little before getting together with Walt. For Hartley, the best way to clear his mind was through vigorous exercise. Obviously, he didn't have time to go to the gym at this very minute, but he did have time for a nice brisk walk. And it was a beautiful day to boot.

He popped into the stairwell and shot down the fifteen flights to the street. Hartley always took the stairs instead of the elevator, to go up as well as down. For the next forty minutes, he walked briskly, swinging his arms and relaxing his shoulders. Using tips he had picked up through a stress-reduction seminar, he breathed fully and deeply from his abdomen, concentrating only on his breathing and shutting off all his other thoughts and worries.

He arrived back at the Midland office feeling greatly invigorated and climbed up the fifteen flights with renewed energy, hardly breaking a sweat.

Everybody had already left for the day. It was the start of the weekend, after all. But Walt was still beavering away in his corner suite. When he heard Hartley in the hallway, he called out to him in his booming voice and waved him into the office.

"So, Hartley, my man, how's it coming along? How's the team treating you?" Walt gave him a big slap on the back. "I'm sure after all these meetings that I've seen you going back and forth to all week, you've managed to convince everyone of the brilliance of your plan."

"Well, Walt. It's not quite so simple," Hartley said. He proceeded to describe the various reactions he'd encountered. Maria supported it wholeheartedly. Joe had come around and was more than willing to give it a try. But Heddy still seemed opposed.

As Hartley went through this, Walt was jotting some things down on the notepad on his desk.

Walt said, "Even without Heddy's support, we still have a majority of top management on side. We can go ahead and start implementing this right away. What're we waiting for?"

"Walt, I understand your impatience," Hartley answered. "But my experience has proven that it's no good to force a program like this through without buy-in from all the top managers, especially managers like Heddy who hold such sway among the staff. By the way, did you hear about her mother's collapse?"

"Yes, poor Heddy," Walt said. "Maggie told me what happened. The poor gal's got her plate full right now. I must remember to send them some flowers," he added, making another note on his pad.

"Give me another week, Walt," Hartley said. "I know that with a bit more time, I can bring Heddy around."

"Okay, but just a week, you hear," Walt replied. "I'm champing at the bit to get this baby in place . . . and to start saving money."

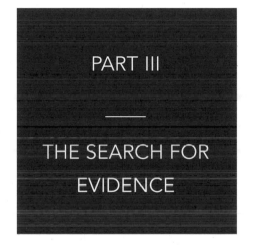

PART III

———

THE SEARCH FOR

EVIDENCE

Chapter 20: A New Joint Venture

Hartley's cultural audit of Midland wasn't the only thing keeping Walt busy these days. At the same time as this was going on, Walt also kept in regular touch with Mike in Austin. The two CEOs were extremely motivated to find another suitable project for which they could submit a joint-venture bid. They were especially motivated because of the changes underway at Midland. Mike was eager to demonstrate to Walt the effectiveness of the healthcare plan risk-management model. And Walt was excited about testing out Hartley's ideas to see if they would help his company's competitiveness. Especially after the letdown of losing the Dallas interchange bid, Walt really felt that, as a leader, he was sorely lacking the competitive edge.

Mike and Walt regularly scoured the construction news wires for notices of upcoming construction projects being tendered across the United States. But, as luck would have it, the next opportunity for a suitable joint venture came up close to home for both of them.

It was a lane expansion of a portion of US Interstate 10, the highway running between Phoenix and Tucson, a project worth a cool $350 million. It would more than make up for the disappointment of having lost the bid on the Dallas interchange.

Since the new project was based on Walt's home turf in Arizona, it only made sense that Midland would be the lead partner on the deal. Both Walt and Mike thought this was a good idea. It would be another means of proving the validity of the healthcare-plan risk-management model that Hartley represented.

"Imagine, Walt: With the combination of our two companies on this project, we're sure to have the bid locked up," Mike enthused. The two men were on the phone, finalizing last-minute plans for Walt to visit Mike's offices the next day. They were going to tour a Cora Construction job site of similar dimensions to the Arizona project.

Chapter 21: Down to Business

Walt was in a great mood as he flew out to Austin the next day. He had decided not to take the company jet, seeing as how Midland was having some cash-flow problems. Normally, this would have been more than enough to make Walt grumpy and miserable. But lately, he had been feeling so energetic that it took a lot more than the usual triggers to bring him down. Walt cabbed it into downtown Austin from the airport. When he arrived at the Commerce Building, he took the elevator up to Mike's office on the eighteenth floor.

Tracey, Cora's long-time receptionist, knew Walt well and knew that he was coming for a meeting with the boss. She gave him a big smile when he arrived and waved him right through to Mike's corner office.

Mike's door was open. He had been expecting Walt, but since Walt was usually a few minutes late for everything, Mike had figured he had time for a few phone calls before his joint-venture partner arrived. Mike was still on the phone, with his back turned to the doorway, when Walt let himself into the office and quietly sat down in one of the leather chairs by the window.

When Mike got off the phone and swiveled around, he jumped with surprise. It wasn't just that he hadn't heard Walt arriving; it was also that he didn't exactly recognize the man sitting in front of him.

"Walter," Mike said with a grin and whistled. "I do believe you're looking very fine, indeed."

"Ah, Mike," Walt replied, "you can go ahead and say it. You won't hurt my feelings. I've lost some weight. Yes, indeed I have. And I plan on losing some more. This Hartley fellow has some great ideas, and I must say I've been feeling like a new man."

"Walt, that's one of the things I admire about you," Mike said. "You're not afraid to give credit where credit is due."

Walt responded, "Well, if we're going to turn this ship around, then I'm going to have to be at the wheel, be a leader, and set the example."

At this point, there was a knock on the door, and both men looked up. It was Mike's assistant, Suzanne, who was bringing in the printed versions of their itinerary for the day.

"Have a seat, Suzanne," Mike said to her. Then he turned to Walt and explained, "Walt, over the next day, I'd like you to hear some of the success stories we're very proud of at Cora about how our staff here has thrived under the corporate wellness plan. Suzanne's is a great example, and I want you to hear it. But it's just one of many. Amita Dexter, one of our top engineers, will join us in a minute to tell us about *her* experience."

With interest, Walt leaned back in his armchair to hear Suzanne's and Amita's stories.

Chapter 22: Conquering Diabetes

As told to Walt by Suzanne Tremblay, administrative assistant, Cora Construction:

When I first started working at Cora Construction three years ago, I was in a really bad place in my life. I was only thirty-seven years old, but I felt so much older. I was a single mother of a teenage son. We used to be so close. But when he hit his teens, we started to grow apart. Now we were fighting constantly. Maybe because of that, or maybe for other reasons, my relationship with the man I'd been living with for the past five years ended. I went on a spending spree to make myself feel better but only ended up deeper and deeper in debt. I saw no light at the end of the tunnel—none. All the stress in my life was weighing me down, literally. I let myself go. I stopped paying attention to what I ate, and my weight kept creeping up. First an extra pound or two. Then an extra five. I kept on gaining more and more.

Junk food—food that was just plain bad for me—was all around, and it became my biggest comfort. I was working at another company back then—I don't want to mention the name so that nobody there gets insulted by what I have to say about it now. Everybody there was really into comfort food. Our jobs were pretty monotonous, so we were always bringing in baked goods to celebrate somebody's birthday or somebody's kid's birthday. We even brought in cookies and cakes when there was nothing to celebrate.

And my boss, thinking he was creating a job perk for us and trying to keep us motivated, was always splurging for lunch, thinking he was doing us a favor. Of course, it was always takeout: hamburgers and fries one day, fried chicken the next, pizza after that. The whole nine yards. Oh, we thought it was great. The office was in a strip mall in the middle of nowhere, and this way we didn't have to worry about making a lunch to bring in or going out to buy one.

Of course, after eating like that every day, we'd all be having a massive energy crash when 3:30 came around, just like clockwork. That's when we all would hit the vending machines in the company kitchen. I swear there would almost be a traffic jam in there. We'd be loading up on junk: candy bars, cola, chips—Triple C, we called it. "It's time for the Triple C," somebody would say, and we all thought that was so cute and funny.

Oh, it was fun at first, but I didn't realize what a slippery slope it was.

You see, I had never had to watch what I eat. I had always prided myself on having a great metabolism. Even after my son was born, I dropped the pregnancy weight in a flash. I never had to diet. Nothing.

I never thought I'd be fat. And while I was piling on the pounds, I just refused to think about it. But then, one day, nothing in my closet fit me anymore. I mean nothing. I had given up my hobbies, like gardening and soccer, because getting around was so hard. Also, to tell you the truth, I was too embarrassed by the way I looked. My son was too, and he sort of dropped hints about that, so I stopped going to PTA meetings too. I just stayed at home and watched TV. I was always feeling light-headed, dizzy, and irritable. I figured it was all that TV.

I knew I had to try to lose weight, but it was so hard at my office. In fact, that's one of the reasons I ended up leaving. There was still all that junk food around me all the time. The smell of hamburgers and pizza at lunch would drive me crazy. And by 2 P.M., my resolve would be cracking, and I would be so tempted to eat things that were off-limits that instead I'd stuff myself on things I could eat, even if I wasn't hungry for them. It seemed I didn't have any willpower. Even though everybody knew I was trying to lose weight, they'd still try to shove cookies and stuff at me. "Oh, you can't live just on carrot sticks," they'd say. "Have a cookie. Just one."

Luckily for me, I found out about this job at Cora Construction. And by some stroke of luck, I ended up getting the job. The first thing I noticed about the office on my very first day (I had been too nervous to look around during my interview) was how fit and healthy everybody looked. The girl who was showing me around told me the company would pay for my membership to a gym if I used it at least two times a week. That sounded like a great idea, but I was way too embarrassed to be seen at a gym.

Then she showed me the office kitchen. There were no vending machines, no bulk boxes of candy bars and chips on the counter, and no pop in the fridge. Instead, the fridge had loads of fresh fruit and yogurt. The cupboards were full of plain nuts—plain almonds, not barbecue peanuts. There was cereal, protein bars. There were three blenders on the counter and recipes for smoothies posted on the bulletin boards.

I was told about their wellness program and figured I had nothing to lose. I went for my biometric testing, and they got me on a scale, and I just wanted to sink into the ground and die when I saw it go past 200. But it didn't end there. They did some blood work and then told me I had to go see my doctor. The doctor dropped the bombshell: I had developed diabetes—type 2 diabetes. "Poor lifestyle choices," she said. "Pathetic lifestyle choices" is what she should have said.

She put me on diabetes medication and warned me that I had to start losing weight—or else. So I started going to the gym, really early in the morning, when there were fewer people there. At first, I'd just walk on the treadmill for ten minutes and be exhausted. But then I'd come into the office and have a smoothie and feel better. Somehow, I started to drop a few pounds, and then I started to feel better about myself.

This inspired me to go to the gym more often and even to get a personal trainer there. With her help, my workout intensified, and the weight started to drop off more quickly.

I'm proud to say that over the last couple of years, I've lost fifty-five pounds. I want to lose ten more. My depression has lifted. I started dating again. My relationship with my son improved dramatically. Not only am I back to taking him to his soccer games, but I've even joined a league myself. And now we don't drive to the games. We take our bikes instead.

And the best news of all is that when I was last at the doctor, she told me that since I was managing my diabetes so effectively with diet and exercise, I could stop taking my oral medication.

It truly feels like a miracle sometimes how my life has turned around. But then I look at the situation more rationally and I realize that all these good things came about through a combination of things: Mike Lopez, the work environment at Cora Construction, the corporate culture here, all the wellness programs, and the example and the encouragement of my colleagues. All these things have helped so much. But I guess the bottom line is that I also helped myself.

Chapter 23: Conquering High Blood Pressure

As told to Walt by Amita Dexter, structural engineer, Cora Construction:

My name is Amita Dexter, and I am a structural engineer at Cora Construction. I grew up in India, in Delhi, and came to the United States almost thirty years ago to go to university in California. My uncle's family was already living there. They told my parents of the excellent educational opportunities in the United States, especially for women. So I left my large family behind and came here at the age of seventeen. It was quite nerve-racking, I must admit. At first, I was quite lonely to be so far away from home. But soon I met new friends, including Ken Dexter. He was in my class at university, and we started hanging around in the same group. Eventually, we started going out, and then we got married. I guess at that point, I realized I wouldn't be going back to India. We now have three children, aged twelve to seventeen—two daughters and a son.

I've always considered myself to be in fairly good health, except for one bad habit that I unfortunately found my way into while I was still in university. It was at the beginning of second year that I started to smoke. At first it was just a social thing at parties and in social situations because those kinds of settings always made me a bit nervous. Plus smoking felt to me like a very emancipated kind of thing. My parents would have been very upset with me if they had ever found out. Women in their social circles in India didn't smoke.

Before I knew it, I was hooked. Especially when things got tough at university around exam time, having a smoke was often the only way to calm my nerves. Ken never smoked. He was always telling me how much he hated it. So did my kids, from the time they were little.

I tried many, many times to quit but without success. I guess my body was too addicted to the nicotine. But I had cut back significantly, to less than a pack a day. I used to smoke two packs a day, easily. But I'd never had any health scares, no cancer scares. And I was very active, biking and in-line skating with my kids. I thought I was one of the lucky ones whose body could ignore the dangers of nicotine. And, generally, I was a very happy person. I loved my family. I loved my job, even though I took my responsibilities at work very seriously. I guess you could call me a perfectionist.

Well, about eighteen months ago, I was working overtime on a big project. I had spent many late nights in a row sitting in front of my computer revising drawings.

One evening, out of nowhere, my right shoulder totally seized up. I thought I was just overtired and could sleep it off. But the next morning, I couldn't move it at all. I was forced to go to the doctor, something I didn't do very often because I had never had any health scares.

He poked around my shoulder, showed me some stretching exercises, and recommended a massage therapist. Since I was there, he said he would just do a few standard tests to check my all-round health. So I thought, "Why not? I'm here anyway." One of them was measuring my blood pressure. He spouted some numbers at me, but they didn't mean anything. Even though I'm an engineer and good with numbers, blood pressure is something I know nothing about.

He repeated the numbers again, this time with a more serious look, and asked me, "Do you know what that means, Amita?" I admitted that I didn't.

"Unfortunately, you appear to have dangerously high blood pressure and could be at serious risk for complications."

"Complications?" I stuttered. "Like what?"

"Well, heart disease, for one. Heart failure. Stroke," he said.

I was so shocked. I thought these were old people's diseases, things that happened primarily to men.

The doctor filled me in on a lot of things, about how high blood pressure wasn't something you could feel, but it was something you could control. He talked about the connection between high blood pressure and salt consumption. And I do have to admit that since coming to the States, I had gotten into the habit of using salt on everything since the food felt so bland compared to the spices back home.

The doctor also said that with my South Asian background, I may carry a greater genetic risk of high blood pressure. And then he said what I really didn't want to hear: that smoking was one of the worst things for it.

Well, I couldn't do anything about my South Asian genes. Cutting back dramatically on the salt wasn't really a problem. I could get in touch with my mother back in India and my aunt in California, and they would be glad to send me all sorts of Indian recipes in which the spicing was so lively that I wouldn't need salt. But the real struggle for me was going to be the smoking. I had tried a lot of things in the past: patches, hypnosis, cold turkey. I was able to cut back but never to quit entirely.

Well, I went back to the office the next day feeling very depressed. But it was right around this time that Cora had just started its wellness program. At first I wasn't even going to sign up for it, even with the $100 incentive on my insurance premiums. But the day right after that horrible doctor's appointment, I read some more of the wellness literature that was still in the in-box of my e-mail, and I realized this program could help me quit smoking.

I was assigned a wellness advocate. His name was Larry. We hit it off right away. The thing I really liked about him was that he had been a smoker himself. So when he gave me advice, it didn't sound pious. He knew where I was coming from. He suggested I try the patches again—a new brand that was just on the market with way better results. But he suggested I do that with a combination of a few other techniques that I hadn't ever considered in the past.

One of them was setting goals in a journal. Now, it sounded pretty corny, but I got into the habit of carrying a little notepad around with me. The size and shape felt like a pack of cigarettes and somehow assuaged me. Every time I felt like a cigarette, I would jot something down in the notepad, anything at all, the first words that popped into my head. It was just a way to count the time while the craving passed. I even held the pen like a cigarette, which, ironically, seemed to help.

Larry also suggested relaxation exercises I could do anytime during the day, even at my desk, when my stress level was building. These would normally be when I would go and have a cigarette. Well, I enjoyed the relaxation exercises so much that I even signed up for classes at a yoga studio in my neighborhood. My parents were very pleased about this since I'd never shown much interest in this part of my Indian heritage.

But do you want to know what was really the tipping point in my battle against cigarettes? A bet with my boss. One day when Mike and I were out on a business lunch, I had to excuse myself to pop out for a cigarette. When I got back to the table, he bet me $500 that I couldn't quit. Well, it wasn't the money that motivated me as much as the challenge of it. As I said, I'm a perfectionist, and I wanted to prove to my boss that I could do it.

Between all of these factors—my family's support; the advice of Larry, my wellness advocate; a new brand of patch; the relaxation and the yoga; and the bet with Mike—I finally had my last cigarette about nine months ago, on New Year's Eve.

I won't say it was easy. But I did it. And Ken and I now have an extra $700 in our family nest egg, between winning my bet with Mike and the $100 insurance-premium incentive we each got back for taking part in the wellness program at Cora, which is also open to spouses.

This money has gone toward our family trip to India. We're going this Christmas, the first time all five of us will go together. That will mark one year that I've been tobacco-free.

My family back in Delhi is so excited at the idea of seeing us all. You know, my parents never knew that I smoked, and one of the reasons I had resisted traveling back to India was that I was worried about hiding my smoking from them. Now, I don't have to worry about this.

I went to the doctor's to check up on vaccinations and other things for the trip, and he pronounced the excellent news that my high blood pressure had cleared up, and I'm off the medication. On top of it, I've lost weight—and so has Ken—since I started cooking a lot more Indian recipes to cut back on the salt. Ken and the kids love the new dishes. We're eating a lot more fresh fruit, vegetables, and legumes, since these are big in Indian cuisine. Good-bye, middle-aged bulge. We've dropped about thirty pounds between the two of us.

I feel like a new woman. And I feel I can live up to my name, Amita. In Hindi, it means "limitless and without boundaries."

Chapter 24: En Route to the Construction Site

After Amita had left Mike's office, Walt sat in his chair, looking solemn and not saying a word. Finally, Mike asked, "Well, Walt, what did you think?"

Walt replied with a fairly brusque tone, "Yup. They were interesting stories. They opened my eyes to some things. But I also told myself—and don't take this the wrong way, okay, Mike?—I told myself that these were both women's experiences, and both of them work mostly in an office setting. I'm wondering how the guys in the field would react to all this wellness stuff. I mean, their conditions are so different. They're on their feet all day outside, not in an office. And, not to resort to clichés or anything, but there are a lot of macho attitudes among the guys."

Mike was nodding as Walter spoke. He answered with a serious tone, "You're absolutely right, Walt. These are issues that we've been dealing with, and we believe we've made significant inroads. Now, if you're up for it, why don't we take a couple of hours and drive out to a job site that's very similar to the new one that we'll be bidding on in Arizona? We'll have a chance to get some data there that's still missing from our bid. But you'll also get a chance to talk to some of the guys out in the field and see how they've experienced the wellness initiatives here at Cora."

Walt was up out of his chair and gathering his things even before Mike could finish speaking. "Now you're talking, Mikey. There's nothing I hate more than sitting around in an office, especially on a gorgeous day like today. Gosh, I love the nuts and bolts of this business. I even love the smell of construction sites."

Mike smiled. He did too, even though he tended to express it in a different way than Walt.

They made their way down to the below-ground parking lot in the Commerce Building, and Mike led the way over to his truck.

Walt said with a grin, "Oh, we're going to drive? For a second, I thought you were going to pull out a bike for me and that we'd cycle over to the site."

Mike laughed. "Well, maybe next time, Walt, if we have more time. But we've got a deadline for this bid. And time is money, right?"

Walt replied with gusto, "Absolutely, Mike. Ab-so-lutely."

During the forty-five-minute drive to the site, they left aside the subject of wellness for a bit and continued to work on their joint venture for the Arizona project. Mike drove while Walt peppered him with questions and noted responses down on his PDA.

At one point, Walt's phone went off, and he took the call. "Hey, Maggie. What's up?" he answered cheerfully.

But then his voice got more somber. "Poor Heddy," he said into the phone. "Her mother's health has been giving her so many worries. You tell her to take the week off and stay home and get everything back in order on that front. That way, she'll be back at the office, ready to work, by the time I get home from this Texas trip."

Walt added, "And did you have a chance to send out those flowers to Heddy's place? Wonderful, Maggie. You're the best. Hold down the fort, and I'll see you in a couple of days."

When Walt ended the call, Mike looked over to him and asked, "Everything okay?"

Walt mumbled, "Pretty much. It's just my HR manager's out of commission for the next week or so, at precisely the time when we really need her at the office. But the poor gal. Her husband's home on sick leave after bypass surgery. Heddy's also taking care of her aging mother, who lives with them, and the old woman was just found in a diabetic coma by their teenage son. When it rains, it pours, huh?"

Mike answered with compassion in his voice. "Yes, that certainly sounds like a heavy burden. We've had some cases like that at Cora. But Hartley's program has done a lot to help them out, not just our employees, but their extended families as well."

As Mike said this, he was pulling the truck off the main highway onto a service road where a lot of heavy construction was going on. All kinds of machinery with the Cora logo stretched up and down the road as far as the eye could see in both directions.

Walt whistled. "So this is it, huh, Mike?"

Mike said, "Yes, this is our project. And I hope we'll be doing the same kind of thing on your turf in Arizona soon. Now, hop out, and I'll show you around. I also want you to meet a couple of guys here who can tell you about their wellness experiences, which will complete the picture that Suzanne and Amita gave you back at the office."

Walt nodded. "Sounds great, Mike. But before we get started, I could sure do with a coffee. Or if there's no decent coffee on the go, maybe an energy drink or something. That stuff tastes like cough syrup, but it sure does give you a caffeine boost. Say, it's going on 2:30. Do you have a vending truck that'll be coming by any-time soon?"

Mike said, "Those vending trucks. The stuff they sell on them could harden your arteries just by looking at it. I won't let them onto my job sites anymore. And you know what? The workers don't complain. Instead, we've set up some heavy-duty fridges in the site trailer and made sure they're always full of good, healthy snacks.

Here, help yourself to some almonds before we go meet the fellows. That'll get your blood sugar up if you're feeling sluggish."

Walt took some almonds from the bag that Mike was holding out to him. He helped himself to a cold bottle of spring water from the fridge. And Mike was right: In five minutes he was raring to go again.

Chapter 25: Conquering Metabolic Syndrome

As told to Walt by Manuel [Manny] Rodriguez, foreman at Cora Construction:

My name is Manuel Rodriguez, but everyone calls me Manny. I've been a foreman with Mike Lopez's company for about fifteen years. I'm forty-five years old and married to Juanita, a wonderful woman whose family immigrated to Texas from Mexico just like mine. We have two amazing sons, one twelve and the other fourteen.

I like my job. I like working outside. I like building things and fixing things traits I got from my father and my grandfathers, I suppose.

My big hobby is soccer. I play in a league and coach my kids' teams too. We have a great time on weekends at tournaments. After the games, we'll all get together at someone's house: all the players and their parents, and the coaches and the refs. We'll get the authentic Mexican cooking going and have ourselves a real feast.

Juanita is an excellent cook and knows all the favorite recipes from our homeland. Often, the after-party tournaments go on late into the night. The kids play together like cousins. The adults hang around, drink some beer, and make some music. That's my other love: music. I play the accordion, and my favorite things to play are the old Mexican songs from when my parents were young. I guess they're coming back into fashion now. We'll get singing and dancing. And the kids will laugh at us at first, but they'll end up joining in eventually.

I suppose between the soccer, the dancing, and the physical work that I do, I figured I was in good enough shape. Sure, I'd put on a few pounds—maybe about ten— since my twenties, but I wasn't nearly as bad as some of the guys I saw on the job, with their beer guts and all the fast food they eat. And on top of it, I never started smoking, and I don't drink very much either, except for these weekend parties that I just described.

So I was really shocked when I found out I had something called metabolic syndrome. I had never even heard of this before.

It all started when I was getting my biometric testing done for Cora's wellness program. After the tests, they said I was high risk and that I should go see my doctor. At first, I didn't like being called "high risk" because I always figured I was doing okay for a guy in his forties. But I followed their advice and went to see my doctor. He was the one who told me about metabolic syndrome. He said it was a relatively newly recognized condition that the medical researchers had identified. It had a couple of different names too, not just metabolic syndrome. They also called it Syndrome X. Basically, it meant that my blood pressure and triglycerides were too high, my good cholesterol was too low, and I had a high level of abdominal fat. All this could lead to stroke, diabetes, heart disease, and kidney disease.

"But, doc," I asked him, "where does it come from?"

Well, he said that Hispanics had a higher predisposition to metabolic syndrome. But he also said that my lifestyle had a lot to do with it too. Too many calories, not enough exercise.

When I went home to break this to Juanita, she was really worried and confused too. She had always figured that we ate pretty well, a lot of homemade, old-style stuff.

Juanita also decided to sign up for the program, and she turned out to be "medium risk" because her cholesterol was too high, although not as bad as mine. Well, like most women, Juanita was a lot more collected than I was. She got me to calm down a little about feeling that I was being labeled. And she encouraged me to focus on all the good we could get from the program.

The great thing was that we had access to our very own wellness advocate, a gal we really got to like. It turns out Juanita and I could even schedule our calls with her together, like a conference call. We would talk for about forty minutes every month or so, and she taught us so many practical things about healthy eating that we never would have really understood on our own.

She taught us easy-to-remember terms like good cholesterol, which is the kind whose presence is raised in the bloodstream by monounsaturated fats such as olive oil, and bad cholesterol, which is the kind raised by saturated fats such as lard. It turns out that the lard was a big part of the problem in our diet because it is such a staple of Mexican cuisine. Some of our favorite recipes, like tamales and refritos (refried beans), really depended on the lard for their authentic taste. But Juanita and I decided we would be ready to sacrifice authenticity for our health. And, in short order, we managed to cut the lard out of our diets completely.

Our wellness advocate also suggested that we expand our cooking repertoire past Mexico's borders. Juanita and I have had fun doing that. We'll go online and look for healthy recipes. And we've cut out the junk food completely.

As part of the wellness program we use a kinetic activity monitor, called a KAM. You just put it on your belt like a pager. It measures the rate and intensity of all physical activity (except in water), and you enter how many servings of fruits and vegetables you have each day.

After a year on this program, it was time for the yearly blood check for the next wellness phase. It turns out that both Juanita and I had our health problems under control. Her cholesterol was down to normal levels. And

I was beating this metabolic syndrome thing. We even "graduated" in the wellness program, from our higher risk levels to low risk.

Now, Juanita and I go to the gym together. The evenings when we're not at the gym, we enjoy the walking program that the wellness advocate got us into.

We still keep in touch with our wellness advocate, although not every month because we're not in the medium- and high-risk categories anymore.

Oh, yeah, and the other great thing that's come out of the wellness program is that I've been identified as one of the success stories at Cora. Mike Lopez asked me to be a mentor for new guys starting up at the company and the guys on my crews who are still kind of suspicious of this whole wellness idea because it's not something they've ever heard of before. Well, even these holdouts were champing at the bit to sign up for wellness when they heard some of the great stuff I told them about from my own experience.

It feels good to be giving something back, especially after all the help people gave me and my family to get our health back on track.

Thanks, Mike, for having the vision and the leadership to bring wellness to Cora.

Chapter 26: Conquering High Cholesterol

As told to Walt by J.J. Barnes, machine operator at Cora Construction:

My name is James Jamila Barnes, J.J. for short. I'm thirty-four years old. I was born in Brooklyn, New York, but my family hails from Louisiana. I ended up coming back south myself in my early twenties. I didn't really know what I wanted to do with my life other than play music. I've been playing guitar since I was twelve, and my specialty is the blues.

I ended up in Austin about ten years ago because of the amazing live music scene. Amazing Austin. Awesome Austin, that's what I say. But even here, it can be pretty hard to make a decent living on music alone. So when a buddy of mine got a job working construction, I tagged along too. And I ended up liking it.

I've been working as an equipment operator at Cora Construction for going on ten years now. I like the job, even if it can get kind of monotonous. Sure, you get to be outside instead of stuck in some office. But really, when you think about it, you're sitting in the cab fiddling with the joystick all day.

Other than my work, I've gone through my fair share of ups and downs lately. Stella, my girlfriend, moved away about a year ago and took our little girl with her. Stella said she was missing her momma and family back in New York too much. But the truth was that we'd been fighting a lot too. I'd come home from work all stressed out and tired. And so I'd veg out in front of the TV all night. Nicky was just a baby back then, and Stella was taking care of her all day. I guess I didn't help out as much as I could have, around the house or with the baby.

I'm still hoping the two of them will move back to Texas one day. Who knows? The one thing I do know is that I sure do miss them a lot. And my life hasn't been the same since they've been gone.

I wasn't really interested in the wellness program. I'd only joined because my foreman had told me that it was a good idea and that he was signing up. I respected the man because he had always given me good advice and been there to help me when I needed it. It wasn't really my scene, counting calories and stuff. Stella used to do that, and it drove me crazy. To tell you the truth, I didn't really bother reading all the pamphlets they'd send around. But some of the guys on the site told me they were doing it anyway, mostly to get the discount off their insurance premiums. Well, it's not going to buy a new car, but it's better than nothing. I figured I could use that money to buy some extra nice Christmas presents for Nicky so that she doesn't forget her daddy while she's away. Well, I got a big shock when I completed my biometric testing. After completing the cholesterol screening, the nurse immediately referred me to my doctor, who told me my cholesterol was way too high. That gave me a jolt. I didn't even know exactly what cholesterol was, except that both my grandma and grandpa died of heart problems—that's on my mother's side.

The doc threw all sorts of numbers and terminology at me. High density, low density—I had trouble keeping it all straight. The part that I did understand was when he said I could be heading for an early heart attack if I didn't watch myself. He said I had to start watching what I ate and exercising a lot more regularly.

As I said, my family's from Louisiana, so soul food was my weakness: fried chicken, croquettes, hush puppies. Stella was the one who used to do all of the cooking around the house. After she moved out, I started eating mostly takeout, at home and at work. I ended up bringing a lot of snack food in my lunch box too just because it would break up the day. I got hooked on all of that stuff. And I stopped playing basketball because I was feeling so low with Stella and Nicky away. So before I knew it, I had put on twenty-five pounds. Well, I'm pretty tall, and it didn't show all that much. But the doctor noticed, I can tell you that.

The one thing that had caught my interest about the wellness program at Cora was the free gym membership. Since I was all alone at home anyway now, I started going to the gym after work, just doing some weights on my own. I would see guys playing pickup basketball, but I didn't feel like hanging out with them. I guess I was still depressed about Stella and Nicky. But one day, I noticed a sign for one-on-one boxing with a guy who used to be a local champ. Well, I used to watch boxing with my grandpa when I was a kid. I figured, "What have I got to lose?" So I signed up for that.

Strapping on some gloves and stepping into the ring was a fantastic feeling. And I really hit it off with Freddy, the ex-champ. He reminded me a lot of my grandpa. Before I knew it, I loved the gym so much that I was getting up early to go there in the morning too. I was lifting weights, and I ended up playing basketball again and making some new friends. I wasn't feeling so lonely anymore. And the days at work were going by faster too.

At this point, they were having wellness meetings on the site every week. They'd tacked them on to a safety meeting. I ended up picking up some good pointers even though I hadn't ever thought nutrition would be my cup of tea.

But the thing was that I had already started to lose weight by going to the gym. I had started to feel better about myself, and I wanted to lose some more. The doc's warnings about cholesterol were in the back of my mind too. I learned some easy tips, like how to buy a healthy lunch at a convenience store if I'm running late. In the past, I would have gotten a big bag of chips, a cola, and a candy bar. Now I'll get some skim milk; even if it's not my favorite thing to drink, it gives me a big boost of protein energy. I'll get some water too and a low-fat, sugar-free yogurt, some plain almonds, and an apple.

I'm also staying away from processed food. The more I heard about all the junk they add to fast food, the grosser it made me feel. And I figured I could do some cooking myself. Now, I haven't turned into Emeril or anything, but even simple recipes like grilled chicken and fish are better than takeout. And, I've rediscovered some vegetables from my childhood, like kale and collard greens. It turns out they're really good for you.

The last time I was talking to Stella on the phone and told her I had started cooking, she sounded really surprised, but in a good way. She also told me I was looking real good in the photo I had sent her at Christmas.

Things are going much better between us, and though I don't want to jinx anything, I'm hopeful that we'll be back together again soon.

More good news is that my doctor told me my bad cholesterol is coming down. I still don't know all that much about the fancy details about cholesterol. But I guess I'm doing something right with the kinds of simple changes I've made.

Chapter 27: Firming Up the Bid

Walt was uncharacteristically quiet on the way back to Austin from the construction site. Mike was a bit worried that maybe he'd laid it on too thick, having Walt talk to all the folks today about their experiences with the wellness program at Cora Construction. Maybe Walt found it all a bit too touchy-feely for his taste, Mike told himself. Maybe Walt was trying to figure out how to bring up the idea that he and Mike weren't suitable business partners after all.

Mike kept his hands firmly on the steering wheel and stared at the road ahead. He wondered how he would approach the Arizona highway project if Walt decided to pull out of the joint venture.

While Mike was lost in his own thoughts, Walt was asking himself if Mike was reconsidering embarking on a joint venture with an old dinosaur like himself, so stuck in his ways. "Where have I been all this time?" Walt thought. "Why haven't I heard about wellness?

Why haven't I heard about proactive healthcare-plan risk management?"

Of the two men sitting silently, side by side in the truck, Walt was the one more likely to say what was on his mind. So he was the one to break the silence. "Listen, Mike. There's something I've been meaning to tell you all day."

"Yes, Walt," Mike answered as neutrally as possible, bracing himself for the bad news.

"I really, really have to thank you for taking the time to introduce me to these folks today and for having them share their stories with me."

"You mean, you found it worthwhile?" Mike couldn't hide his surprise.

"Are you kidding me? It was really a turning point."

Mike laughed in relief. "That's great, Walt. I was kind of thinking that maybe all this talk about health and fitness was turning you off the idea of working together."

"You're crazy, Lopez," Walt answered with a grin. "But to tell you the truth, I was kind of thinking you wouldn't want to be working with an old geezer like me."

Both of them laughed in relief. They were approaching the city now, and Mike asked Walt, "Do you have some time to come back to the office and fool around with some numbers?"

"Yes sirree," Walt answered. "We have a bid we have to finish putting together."

PART IV

THE FINAL
CHALLENGES

Chapter 28: Hartley Helps Heddy

While Walt was in Austin meeting with Mike to go over their new joint-venture bid on the Arizona highway expansion, things hadn't slowed down at the Midland head office in Phoenix on the healthcare insurance front.

Maria, the risk manager, was busy reviewing the list that Hartley had given her of third-party vendors who could provide wellness programs to Midland employees. Joe, the CFO, was test-driving some of the claims data-analysis software that Hartley had recommended he check out.

Heddy was off on an emergency family leave for the whole week taking care of her convalescing mother. So Hartley knew he wouldn't have a chance to meet with her in person within the deadline that Walt had given him to convince Midland's executive team of the merits of proactive healthcare-plan risk management.

But Hartley had other ideas about how to get through to Heddy.

He was a man with a great deal of empathy, and winning her over to his side of the wellness debate wasn't his only motivation. Hartley really did feel for Heddy, with all the stress and worry she was facing on the home front. And he knew he had access to the kind of advice and information that could help Heddy tremendously.

So, in a very casual and nonaggressive way, he contacted her by e-mail. His first message made no mention of corporate wellness. He simply asked how her mother was doing.

Even while she was away from the office, Heddy was still checking her work e-mail on a regular basis. She was far too much of a perfectionist to let that slide. She was surprised to see Hartley's name pop up in her inbox. And she was even more surprised by the friendly tone of his message. Heddy was sure she had insulted him with her thinly veiled criticisms and brusqueness, especially the last time they had met, the day her mother had taken ill.

Heddy responded in an equally friendly manner. She told Hartley that her mother seemed to be recovering physically but was quite depressed by the downturn in her health. Heddy added that her son was having some trouble too, that he was feeling really quite traumatized about having been the one to find his grandmother collapsed on the kitchen floor.

Heddy was the kind of person who let her guard down more easily in e-mails than face-to-face. She ended her note to Hartley by saying, "It's pretty overwhelming, all this stuff going on with my mother. You know what I mean?"

Hartley responded to her right away. "I do know what you mean, Heddy. Actually, I've gone through practically the same scenario with my mother-in-law, who is also a type 2 diabetic and had a similar collapse. I hope you don't think this is too personal, but if you like, I could suggest some of the things that seemed to work to help Tess's mom."

Heddy was taken aback, but in a good way. She had found Hartley a bit off-putting in her initial dealings with him. So she was surprised that they seemed to be having such a friendly e-mail exchange.

She wrote back to him, "Sure I'd love to hear what worked for you with your mother-in-law."

Over the next few days, Hartley sent her a number of e-mails outlining resources available online. He told her how he and his wife had helped her mother—psychologically, as well as physically—by getting her involved with a seniors' group. "This boosted her morale so much," Hartley wrote. And he told Heddy how he had dealt with his own anxiety during this stressful time by starting to practice stress-reduction techniques, such as deep breathing.

Heddy was impressed by how Hartley was confiding in her about his own anxiety attacks. She decided to look into it.

Chapter 29: Heddy's Change of Heart

Over the next few days, Heddy was surprised to find that things were getting easier at home—in small ways, to be sure, but every little step counted. Her mother's mood was improving. Her son Tom seemed to be back in the swing of things. He'd even aced a test in chemistry, which was usually a subject that gave him a lot of problems.

Heddy had gotten a book on stress reduction out of the library and was reading it with interest. She was even taking the time, during what was surely one of the most stressful weeks of her life, to do some deep breathing. This was the kind of thing she had always intended to do—when she had more time. But the book on mindfulness taught her not to put off learning a valuable coping mechanism at the time when she needed it most. Heddy was amazed at how much such a little thing was helping her, both at the very moment she did it and all through the day.

The last day of her emergency family leave was drawing to a close. Heddy and her husband, Victor, were getting ready to turn in for the night.

Victor was brushing his teeth; Heddy, brushing her hair.

She said to him reflectively, "You know, I really didn't think much of that Hartley guy and his ideas when I first met him. But I have to admit that he's helped me a lot this week."

Victor mumbled, his mouth still full of toothpaste, "That's amazing, Heddy." He rinsed and repeated, "Yeah, it's amazing, especially considering what a crazy week it's been for us.

"And you know something else?" Victor continued. "I've been thinking about this Hartley guy too."

Heddy responded with amazement. "You have, Vic? But you don't have anything to do with him."

"I know, I know," he said. "But while we were in the hospital with Ma the other week, and you were off talking to some nurses, I was so bored with the crummy selection of magazines in the waiting room that I picked up one of those wellness pamphlets you had in your briefcase."

Heddy laughed. "Oh, yeah, I remember that one. Hartley forced it into my hand when we met, and I remember thinking, 'That's pretty forward of him.'"

Victor said, "Well, I got to reading it, Heddy. And it talked about how some of these corporate wellness

programs were open to spouses. And then I got to thinking, 'Well, maybe it would do me some good to get hooked
up with one of these wellness advocates myself.'"

Heddy asked with surprise, "You, Vic? I thought you
hated this kind of touchy-feely stuff."

He answered, "Well, you won't catch me singing
about butterflies and doing headstands or anything,
don't get me wrong. But I do want to get my body back
into shape. This is no way to go on living, sitting on my
butt all day. And I'd like to get back to work. Lose some
weight. And even take my girl out dancing from time to
time."

Heddy smiled. They hadn't been out, just the two of
them, in ages. But in their day, they had ruled the dance
floor with their rumba and cha-cha.

"I'd like that too, Vic," she said. "Thanks for letting
me know what you think about wellness. I'm going to
sleep on it and figure things out in the morning."

They got into bed and turned off the light. And during the next eight hours, both Victor and Heddy enjoyed
the best night of sleep they'd had in a long time.

Chapter 30: Early-Morning Wake-Up

The next day was what Hartley called the Big Meeting. This was when all of the top decision-makers at Midland would get together and weigh in with their thoughts on Hartley's proactive healthcare-plan risk-management program.

All the executives on the team knew that Midland was going ahead with the program, no matter what each one of them might think about it individually. Walt had made it very clear, from the moment he first brought this up with them, that he was on board, all the way, and that this was the direction the company was headed in.

But, as Hartley had explained at the outset, it was much better for the program's success to have as many top managers on side as possible. So the Big Meeting was a big day for Hartley, the day when everyone would see how much luck he'd had through his one-on-one lobbying with the management holdouts.

Hartley had flown into Phoenix from Austin the night before, checked into his hotel, and got to bed early.

He was an early-to-bed, early-to-rise guy just like Mike Lopez, which was another reason the two of them had hit it off from the start.

Hartley's alarm was set for 6:30 A.M. His bad knee had been acting up again, so he was going to go for a swim instead of his usual morning routine on the elliptical machine. He was just getting ready to head down to the pool when the phone in his room rang loudly. Hartley jumped. He wasn't expecting any calls at such an early hour, and he hoped that nothing was wrong at home. He picked up the receiver cautiously.

Walt's somber voice rang down the line. "Hello, Hartley."

Hearing such a serious tone, Hartley's spirits began to sink. The first thought that ran through his mind was that Walt must have already talked to Heddy, who had been resisting his plan from the outset. Heddy must have told Walt that she was still opposed to the idea. Hartley already felt disappointed. He thought he had managed to get through to Heddy at the end.

Finally, Walt broke the silence. He burst out with a whoop, "You did it, Hartley!" Then he added with a laugh, "I had you going for a minute there, didn't I?"

Hartley tried to sound casual as he answered. "Oh, only for a split second, Walt. They warned me that you were a joker."

Walt reverted back to his regular, straightforward voice. "And they warned me that you knew what you were doing. And I must say they were right. I have to admit that when Mike Lopez first told me about you, and then you came in here and went through some of your ideas, there were a few moments when I wasn't sure if we were on the same page.

"But I've changed a lot since then. And I have to admit, I'm a believer now. And it turns out, so is the rest of the team. I ran into Heddy at the gym this morning, if you can believe it. We were both there so early. And we talked about corporate wellness as we were on the treadmills, side by side. Heddy is so gung ho now. She told me how she's going to speak out in favor of the plan at the Big Meeting today. So as soon as our workout was finished, I rushed back to the locker room to call you."

"Whoo-hoo!" Hartley exclaimed. "So Heddy came through."

"Did she ever," Walt responded. "She was saying some pretty nice things about you too."

"Well, I did my best."

Walt ended the call by saying, "I've got to run now. We have the Big Meeting coming up in a couple of hours. See you there."

Chapter 31: New Responsibilities

The Big Meeting turned out to be a huge success. Hartley presented the outcome of the cultural audit and the analysis of the data collected in Step Two. He explained that Midland's plan design was inefficient and that the company should be using a different doctor network. He also explained some of the diseases and conditions that were driving their claims and recommended a new plan design that he had developed using Principal Risk Management's predictive modeling software. The tension and apprehension that had been present among the executive team when Walt had first broken the idea to them about a month ago had dissipated. The kind of suspicion that some people had shown toward Hartley was completely gone. They were treating him like one of the team—a very important member of the team, in fact. A lot of excellent brainstorming took place in the room that day about how to roll out the new program at Midland. Hartley took copious notes, and everybody left the room on a collective adrenaline high.

Afterward, Walt and Hartley got together briefly. Walt said, "I do believe, if my calculations are correct, that with the Big Meeting, we've wrapped up Step Three. So what's the next step in your famous seven-steps-to-corporate-wellness plan?"

"Yes, Walt, you're right. The Big Meeting did mark the end of Step Three," Hartley responded. "Step Four involves appointing someone from among your management team to be in charge of implanting the new proactive healthcare-plan risk-management program at Midland. All staff will be involved, of course, but you need a go-to person to shepherd the whole thing along the way."

"I hear you, Hartley," Walt responded. "Well, Heddy's been great—and as I just told you, she's your biggest fan now—but her plate is pretty full right now, at home and at work. To tell you the truth, I have my eye on Maria. We keep her pretty busy already, but she's dynamic and has got a ton of great ideas. And her record on implementing safety programs has been impeccable."

"I agree with you, Walt," Hartley replied. "That's exactly the way my thinking was going. Maria's an excellent choice. And corporate wellness fits in beautifully with her current responsibilities as the risk manager. A lot of incentives can be doubled up for more effectiveness. But keep in mind that this will involve a fair bit of extra work for Maria, and down the road you'll probably need to consider hiring somebody else to take this on."

"We'll cross that bridge when we come to it," Walt said. "I'm going to call Maria in here right now and tell her so she can get cracking.

"So is that it for Step Four?" Walt asked.

"It is indeed," Hartley said. "We're rolling right along."

Chapter 32: Building Partnerships

Maria was very excited by her new responsibility of being in charge of the wellness program at Midland. She felt it fit in well, in many ways, with her mode of thinking. It was a method of promoting a competitive edge, something she believed in very strongly. But it also looked out for the interests of the workers. She believed in profit, but in profit that was fairly earned and without harmful repercussions.

The very next day, after the Big Meeting and after Walt had told her that she would be spearheading the program, she was on the phone arranging a meeting with Whytes Wellness, the third-party provider with which Hartley's customers collectively contracted. This was Step Five of the seven-step process.

Hartley had explained to Maria the process whereby he had entered into partnership with Whytes. He had had a lot of options when he went out looking for a wellness provider. This was a field that had really taken off in the past five years or so, and there were many options available out there. He and his associates had carefully interviewed five of the top wellness providers in the United States, and these providers had come into Austin to make pitches to Hartley and his board of directors, which consisted of the CEOs and CFOs of his top consulting customers.

Ultimately, they had chosen Whytes. It had been a unanimous decision, Hartley had explained to Maria. What they especially liked about Whytes was the way in which its program addressed the entire spectrum of the fitness equation. Some of the other wellness programs had been skewed one way or the other. It was common knowledge that 20 percent of employees accounted for 80 percent of healthcare costs. The problem with some wellness providers, Hartley explained to Maria, was that most focused almost exclusively on the portion of employees who were at the greatest health risk, arguing that these were the ones driving healthcare costs. Other wellness providers chose to ignore those who were already in poor health, arguing that there wasn't much that could be done about them and that corporate energy should focus on the ones who are in the best shape.

"We didn't like the take-it-or-leave-it approach of either of these options," Hartley had said. "We felt that there had to be a program that addressed both employees 'at risk' and those who weren't. And Whytes Wellness was the one that had come up with a system for targeting both ends."

Maria had agreed with Hartley that this was totally the way to go. And today she was on her way to Whytes to have a tour of its facilities, meet with its staff, and begin mapping out strategies for introducing the Whytes Wellness way to the employees at Midland.

Chapter 33: Visiting Whytes Wellness

Twenty-five-year-old Keisha McFadden had been a wellness advocate at Whytes for three years. She had degrees in nutrition and marketing, and had also completed a program in coaching behavioral change. She was passionate about her work. She loved working with people and helping them bring about positive change in their lives. In many ways, she was a lot like Maria Carrera from Midland, so it wasn't surprising that the two women hit it off well at their first meeting when Maria went to the Whytes offices.

Maria was full of questions for Keisha. "So tell me all about your job. What's it like? What kinds of reactions do you get?"

Keisha answered honestly. "Well, a lot of people are fearful of the Big Brother syndrome and ask us, 'Will you talk to our employers about this?'—which is a totally fair question—and we assure them that this will absolutely never happen.

"And some people just aren't interested in talking about their health with a complete stranger, so a lot of our calls are about relationship-building so that we don't feel like a complete stranger to the person at the other end of the line.

"I'm taking copious notes as I talk to a client so that in further conversations, I'll remember if they have talked about the grandkids they love so much. And maybe, I can then suggest they take the grandkids to the park as part of their exercise goals."

Maria was impressed. "That's really very perceptive of you. That must work well. What are some of the things that don't work so well?"

Keisha answered, "Well, some clients are all or nothing. They want to quit smoking and lose 60 pounds right away, which is just not going to happen. We keep them focused on working on one goal at a time. It's when they feel that they are accomplishing things that they stay on track and don't get overwhelmed.

"We're listening, of course, for bigger issues that could be having a negative impact on their health, things like marital problems, financial worries, and drug and alcohol abuse. For sure, these stresses are all interrelated, but we're not part of the process of getting help for these kinds of issues. But we will most certainly refer them to resources outside Whytes, where they can get this kind of help."

Maria found herself fascinated by the kind of relationship that must develop between the wellness advocate and her clients. She asked Keisha, "Can the clients call you up themselves if they're having a bad day or a crisis or something?"

Keisha responded knowledgeably. "Yes, our program is a two-way street. Our advocates make outreach calls to high-risk individuals, and all employees have unlimited telephone access to our wellness coaches."

Maria looked surprised. "Doesn't that create an incredible burden on your staff?"

Keisha shook her head. "Not really. We've been doing this a long time and our statistics show that the average employee will talk to a wellness coach 3 or 4 times a year and we are staffed accordingly."

"That makes so much sense," Maria said. "I can't wait to get this started at Midland. Now, should we sit down and go through the schedule of how we'll roll this out to all the employees?"

"Let's do it," Keisha said with a grin.

Chapter 34: Announcement to the Staff

Step Six of the seven-step process involved rolling out the program to all employees. Prior to this, members of Midland's executive team had had meetings with the divisional leadership and gotten their "buy-in." Then they'd had a month-long communication campaign, with material such as posters and paycheck stuffers announcing the program. Now it was time to meet with the employees to get them to understand what was in it for them and how the company would benefit. It wasn't only CEOs like Walt who liked to win; the employees did too.

There were about 300 people who worked at Midland and in various different locales across several states, so it wasn't realistic to get all of them together in a single room to roll out the wellness program in one fell swoop.

Besides, as Keisha, the wellness advocate had explained to Maria, the employees' first exposure to the details of the wellness program worked best in smaller group settings. This was, after all, a lot of new information being thrown at them and an entirely new way of looking at their jobs and their lives in general. It was less intimidating if this was done in smaller groups so that the employees felt more at ease to express their opinions and ask questions.

On this day, Keisha and Maria were meeting with a work crew of about fifty based in Tucson. It included experienced foremen who had been in this line of work for going on thirty years, as well as young men with only a couple of months' experience as part of a construction crew. Many of them had Spanish as their first language, so Maria was doing two presentations, one in English and one in Spanish, and made sure she had all the support material available in Spanish too.

The presentation was taking place outside the construction trailer that was their job headquarters. Chairs had been set up for the employees but most were standing and talking in small groups. As Keisha and Maria exited the trailer and took up position on the small landing outside the trailer door, the sound of the chatter died down and people slowly began to take their seats. It wasn't that the mood was unfriendly, per se, just cautious.

But Maria was a familiar face to these workers and a popular manager, so she broke the ice with a couple of jokes, including a Spanish one she had just heard.

Then she got into the meat and potatoes of her presentation. "As you've already heard, Midland is entering an exciting new phase as the company embarks on a different way of managing healthcare insurance. I know that for some of you, this might seem like a risky thing to do, but, believe me, this is a proven method that we've investigated thoroughly. Not only will it save the company money, but it will also put money in the pocket of each and every one of you who chooses to participate. And not only will you benefit from financial incentives, but you'll also be doing yourselves and your bodies a big, big favor by participating. You're going to be decreasing your chances of getting debilitating diseases like cancer, heart disease, and strokes. You're going to lose weight. You're going to have more energy. It's such a fantastic, fantastic opportunity for every one of us. So, with no further ado, I'd like to introduce you to Keisha McFadden of Whytes Wellness, who will explain the nuts and bolts of how to sign up."

Keisha was up next. "As Maria said, we want to help lower the costs of your healthcare insurance, and we'll provide you with discounts on your premiums as an incentive. The thing that will happen today, for those of you who sign up, is that we're going to get a few bits of basic health information from you. We'll begin by checking your biometrics; that's your height, weight, blood pressure, and blood chemistry."

She paused. "The blood-chemistry check will involve a finger-stick blood test, but I promise it won't hurt." Her smiling comment was greeted by more than a few chuckles. Keisha continued, "Then you'll complete a health-risk appraisal form about your lifestyle choices, medical background, etc. We then put the results of the biometric testing together with the information you provide on the form and use this to help us divide you into three groups: those who are low risk, those who are medium risk, and those who are high risk. All of you will get a nineteen-page personal health report. You will also be given something called a KAM. KAM stands for kinetic activity monitor, and it allows you to monitor your daily activity and calorie burn. You also use it to track your nutritional input.

"Now, if you're identified as being high risk, you shouldn't panic. It doesn't mean your situation is dire or desperate or anything like that. It simply means that you could benefit from being hooked up with a wellness advocate, who is someone like me with a background in nursing, nutrition, and exercise physiology. He or she will be your coach. You'll be working one-on-one with your wellness advocate, always over the phone and always at your convenience, to work toward achieving health and fitness goals that you have identified as being your priority. After the initial, getting-to-know-each-other call, you'll be talking to your wellness advocate once a month for about twenty to thirty minutes. You will also have on-going access to something called a health station, where you will be able to track your weight and blood pressure as well as download information from your KAM. Your coach will receive this information as well as information supplied by the company's healthcare providers and use it to assist you in keeping track of your goals, as well as to give you hints on new techniques to try if something isn't working.

"At the end of the year, we'll retest your biometrics and see what kind of progress you've made healthwise. And then, assuming you've maintained the other conditions—things like wearing your KAM, getting a physical, etc.—your insurance discount will continue for the coming year. Our goal is to help you move out of the medium- or high-risk category into the low-risk one.

"For those of you who are low risk or medium risk at the start, you'll always be able to contact a wellness advocate if any questions come up, but you won't have one assigned to you to do one-on-one regular calls. You'll have regular wellness meetings to attend, much like the safety meetings that Maria manages so well, where you'll learn new techniques for optimizing your health, techniques such as journaling. Now this might sound like a funny term to those who haven't heard it before, but it's really very simple. You just keep a little notebook handy and mark down various goals and how you have achieved them. Or if you didn't achieve them, what things got in your way. Believe it or not, journaling is one of the most effective means of breaking out of bad lifestyle habits and embracing healthy ones. There's something about the act of committing something to paper in writing that motivates us to follow through."

Keisha was starting to wrap up. "Now I know that's a ton of new information for a lot of you, and it might seem overwhelming at first. But rest assured that everybody at Whytes Wellness who you'll be working with is a health professional passionate about his or her work. Our job is to get you looking and feeling your best. And, just on a final note, I wanted to remind you that participation in the wellness program is voluntary this year and that all your health information, everything that happens between you and a wellness advocate, is strictly confidential.

"So why don't we break for fifteen minutes and give you a chance to process some of this stuff? Then we'll get back together and go over any questions you might have."

Chapter 35: Let's Do It

After Keisha and Maria finished their presentation, the employees broke up into smaller groups to talk about what they'd just learned. Sure, they had seen company e-mails and pamphlets for some time now saying that this was coming down the pipe, but this was their first face-to-face encounter with the changes ahead, and some of them found it overwhelming.

Carlos, an equipment operator, appeared quite perturbed and told his colleagues, "It sounds totally Big Brother to me. Who are these people, total strangers, who are going to talk to me about whether or not I had a cheeseburger for lunch or a beer after work? And say I do try to quit smoking and then have a bad day and end up bumming some cigarettes—are they going to turn me in to my boss or something like that? Maybe it could even get me fired."

Louis, a well-respected and longtime foreman, responded, "Whoa, Carlos. Calling this a 'Big Brother' move is going way too far. Think about it. The government is always going on about confidentiality. What kind of professional in his or her right mind would try to mess with that? If anything, I bet you they're way more careful about keeping all the medical records top secret. Just to be on the safe side, you know."

Louis continued, "And the other thing we have to remember, guys, is that all of the top brass at Midland has signed up already to do the very same thing: wear the KAM, be weighed, talk to wellness advocates, the works. They'll all be doing that too—Burtinski, Heddy from HR . . ."

"Even Walt Williams?" somebody asked.

"Especially Walt Williams," Louis responded. "I was at the leadership buy-in meeting they just had, and Williams was so gung ho about this, you wouldn't believe it. He's working out every day and drinking smoothies at the office, and has dropped a ton of weight. They have even removed the junk food vending machines at the Phoenix headquarters and replaced them with a supply of healthy food like fresh fruit and energy bars. They're going to do this at all the construction sites too."

"Hoo-boy," Carlos answered. "I guess you're right, Louis. If Williams can do it, so can I. He needed to lose some weight, but I do too."

Chapter 36: Smooth Sailing

Over the next several weeks, Maria and Keisha traveled across the country to visit all the Midland offices and make the wellness presentation to all of the staff. It was a long and tiring process for them, but they were both so enthusiastic about the program they were pitching that listeners never got the impression that the two young women were bored or tired. By the end, when all Midland staff were in the loop, Keisha and Maria sat down with Hartley to calculate the rate of people in the company who had signed up.

Hartley entered some figures into his calculator and let out a whistle: "It's 70 percent."

Maria looked a bit crestfallen and said, "I'm not really sure what we did wrong."

Hartley looked at her with amazement. "You didn't do anything wrong, Maria. Seventy percent is fantastic. Some companies are lucky to get even half of that."

Keisha backed him up. "He's right, Maria. It's a fantastic result. Walt has every reason to be delighted and proud of all your hard work."

Maria did look proud. She said, "So that's it for Step Six, right?"

Hartley answered, "That's right. There's only one step remaining, and that's the simple one of keeping the program running smoothly with regular updates and maintenance as needed. I'm sure that with you in charge, this maintenance stage won't be a problem at all and that the program will continue to grow and prosper.

"And Keisha is right," Hartley said to Maria. "It takes time and leadership to develop a culture of health and fitness. Wellness is a process, just like your safety program. Now let's call Walt in to tell him the great news."

When Walt heard they had arrived at Step Seven, he let out a big whoop of delight. "Hooray! This calls for a celebration. It's funny; in the past, we would have ordered beer, pizza, and an ice-cream cake. But those days are gone. I just discovered a new health-food caterer down the street that makes these amazing fresh fruit trees, like something you might have found on Carmen Miranda's head in those great old movies. I'm going to get Maggie to order us some of those to celebrate."

Chapter 37: The Pyramid Again

That evening, when Walt returned home from work, he was in a terrific mood. So was Louise. Ever since Walt had discovered the benefits of corporate wellness for Midland, he was also following up on them in his personal life. This was inspiring Louise in more ways than one. Not only was it great to have a husband with more energy and vitality, but it also inspired her to watch what she was eating and to take up exercise, something she hadn't done since her college days.

Walt opened up his front door to a delicious smell wafting in from the kitchen. He called out, "Hey, honey, I'm home." But when he got to the kitchen, it was empty. There was a note on the counter that read, "Just popped out to a yoga class. Back by 7. Dinner's in the slow-cooker. Love and kisses, Lou."

Walt wandered over to the slow-cooker and peered in through the glass lid. It looked and smelled wonderful, with lots of green and orange vegetables mixed in with chicken. Walt and Louise were having a great time together now looking for healthy recipes to try out. And they weren't only using the Internet for this. Sometimes after dinner, they'd put on their walking shoes and have a nice stroll over to the public library, which was about thirty minutes away on foot. The library had a fantastic selection of cookbooks, and the librarians had already gotten to know Walt and Louise and would put books aside for them.

Walt was even having a go at being in charge in the kitchen every once in a while, something he'd never had the urge to do before. But he was discovering that he had a knack for it, especially for using fresh herbs, which he would chop up with relish with the new knife that Louise had gotten him just for this.

Normally, if Louise wasn't home when Walt got back from work, he would have poured himself a drink and watched some TV. But it was a beautiful evening outside. He decided to do a little work in the garden until dinnertime.

They had a lovely supper together with just a glass of red wine each. They knew that a glass or two of red wine every night or so was good for preventing heart disease, but they were also aware now of the dangers of overindulging in alcohol—to say nothing of the empty calories.

After dinner, Walt decided to check out his profile on the My Pyramid website. He hadn't done this for a while. But first he had to weigh himself. His clothes were beginning to feel looser again, and he was sure he had lost weight even though he wasn't on an official diet. He had been rather embarrassed about mentioning this to Louise because he felt kind of sheepish that he had let his personal condition slide so much over the last few years. So he sneaked out the scale and got onto it tentatively.

The digital numbers appearing on the screen down by his feet made him rub his eyes and look twice. He had lost twelve pounds just by eating more healthily and being a little more active. And he felt much better too. Walt let out a whoop of laughter just as Louise was passing by.

She asked with bewilderment, "Honey, what's up?" And then, when she stepped into the room and saw the scale, she said, "Oh that's where the scale has gone to. I've been looking for it everywhere."

Walt smiled. "Lou, I've lost twelve pounds. I feel so good."

Louise smiled too. "I know you do, Walt. And you look amazing too."

Epilogue

This time they were in Phoenix, at the Arizona state highway letting. And it was on Walt's turf that the CEOs of Cora Construction and Midland Building Associates were getting together the day before to put the finishing touches on the bid they would be submitting on the Phoenix-to-Tucson highway extension.

Walt suggested that they make it a late-afternoon meeting rather than an evening one. He told Mike, "I'd like to squeeze in a workout after we get together and then have an early night. These highway lettings require a lot of energy and attention. And I don't want anything interfering with that."

Mike answered, "Good plan, Walt. I'm with you there."

So they got together at an outdoor café that Walt had discovered recently near his office. It specialized in fresh salads, fruit juices, and smoothies.

Walt said to Mike with a grin, "Thought you might have a hankering to try out an Arizona smoothie and see how it compares to your Texas ones. They do a lot of great combos here, with both fruits and vegetables. And they give them great names too. One of my favorites is called Rocket Fuel. It's got carrots and apple and ginger for zing. Who needs those canned energy drinks, I say, when you can have one of these babies?"

Walt added, "You know, Mike, I read somewhere that Americans aren't eating nearly as many servings of fruits and vegetables a day as they should. They're missing out on all the amazing antioxidants and disease-fighting agents that you can only get from fruits and veggies."

Mike nodded with a smile. He was really enjoying the tremendous energy for wellness that Walt exuded now. Hartley had really done a great job of getting the ball rolling, but it was Walt himself who deserved the congratulations for embracing it with such genuine, whole-hearted support.

Mike ordered a Rocket Fuel too. It was quite a different sight from the last time the two CEOs had firmed up a bid for a highway letting. This time, instead of meeting at the Lakeview Bar over a glass of wine and a single malt, they went over their final numbers while taking sips of bright orange smoothies.

Things were looking good, and it didn't take much time to get their work done. Walt headed off to the gym, and Mike decided to go back to his hotel, where he would check out the fitness facilities too.

Walt called out, "Remember, Mike, get a good night's sleep, and I'll see you bright and early tomorrow."

The next day, both men managed to fit in a morning workout. They were both in good, happy moods and positively humming with adrenaline as they dropped off the Cora–Midland bid at the desk with the officials from the Arizona Department of Transportation.

Walt sang out to the officials behind the desk, "Take good care of that one. It's a good one."

Walt and Mike accomplished their networking with ease. They ate little; the hotel fare was heavy and not particularly appetizing. As the coffee was being served, the announcer at the front of the room began reading out the project numbers and the winning bids.

The announcer's voice droned on until, finally, she read, "Project ARZ 17-938. Extension of Phoenix–Tucson Highway. State engineer estimates $350 million. We had seven bids submitted on this one."

Walt turned to Mike and gave him a big thumbs-up. Mike returned the gesture with a grin.

The announcement continued: "And the winning bid goes to the joint venture of Midland Building Associates–Cora Construction. Congratulations to the winners."

GETTING INTO SHAPE:

———

THE REAL-LIFE METHOD

Part 1: The Seven Steps of Change

As I've explained in this book's introduction, and, as you've seen throughout the parable about Walt Williams and Midland Building Associates, the thought of change is often intimidating. But embracing the process of change, as Walt learns to do, can bring incredible rewards.

I want to help companies make a difference. I want to show them how to take control of their healthcare insurance—and how to turn crisis situations into win-win propositions for both CEOs and employees. And in order to do this, I have developed a model of change that incorporates the seven steps that Hartley Smith, the healthcare-plan risk-management consultant, outlined in the parable.

These are the seven steps that our fictional CEOs, Mike Lopez and Walt Williams, applied to their companies with great success. But I can guarantee you that I have seen these seven steps applied equally successfully in real-life corporate America.

Step One: Recognize the Risk
You are admitting you have a problem and want to do something about it.

Step Two: Collect the Data
You need to know your employee population in order to prove to yourself and to others that the problem really does exist and to establish a baseline against which your progress can be measured.

Step Three: Ensure Organizational Readiness by Educating CEO and Staff
You are arming the troops to begin fixing the problem.

Step Four: Assign This as Someone's Responsibility within Your Company
You are identifying the main people who will be in charge as you go about fixing the problem. Someone has to lead the effort.

Step Five: Build Partnerships
You are enlisting outside experts to help fix the problems.

Step Six: Install Programs and Procedures
You are acquiring the tools to fix the problems.

Step Seven: Keep Up the Programs with Regular Maintenance
You are putting those tools to good use and measuring your progress. Congratulations. By this time, you are well on your way to fixing your problems.

How Would You Handle a Leaking Roof?

Some readers of this book may not be corporate CEOs, just regular Americans concerned about the state of their personal health and the economic well-being of their workplaces and their country in general. Although corporate leaders set the tone of change within an organization, individuals are a very important part of the process too. So here is an analogy based on regular household maintenance that most everybody can relate to in his or her personal life: how to handle a leaking roof.

Rainy season is coming. Remember how the roof leaked last year and you didn't get around to getting it fixed? Remember all the headaches and damage that created? You know you need to get around to fixing the roof this year; otherwise, you'll have a disaster on your hands. You have recognized your risk. That's Step One.

Well, what if there's no rain this year? Then the leaking roof won't be a problem, will it? But the chances of there being no rain at all ever again are practically nil. If you check through farmers' almanacs and meteorological records on the Internet and in the library, you'll realize that one day, sooner or later, more rain will come. You are collecting the data to support the fact that a problem exists and to establish a baseline for repair. You need to thoroughly examine the roof to determine the extent of the damage and to outline the specifications for the repair. That's Step Two.

Do you have the money to fix the roof? If you don't have the ready cash, do you have access to a loan? What about time and materials? You are making sure that you're organized and have the resources to begin fixing the problem of the leaking roof. That's Step Three.

You have to be out of town on business for most of the coming month, so you won't be around to supervise the roofers. But your spouse will be around, so you decide that it will be his or her responsibility to make sure the work is done properly. You are assigning the roof leak as the responsibility of someone in your household. That's Step Four.

You know you have a leak in your roof. You know you want it fixed. But you are not a roofer and can't do it yourself. So you find a roofer to do it for you. And because there's been some drywall damage to your home's interior from last year's leak, you also track down a housepainter to come in and fix that once the roof work is done. And there's your bank loan that needs to be managed to pay for all of this, so you enlist the help of a financial advisor. You are building partnerships to help fix the problem of your leaky roof. That's Step Five.

It's the big day. Today's the day you're having your new roof installed. You're rolling out your plan. That's Step Six.

Phew! The roofers are gone. You're relieved that that part of it is done with. And you certainly don't want to go through this whole messy process again for as long as you can help it. So you vow to keep the new roof in tip-top shape. You make sure the gutters are cleaned every spring and every fall. You make sure that no animals such as squirrels, raccoons, or birds can access your roof and burrow into it. You're keeping up the regular maintenance. That's Step Seven. Now let's review each of the seven steps in more detail.

Step One: Recognize the Risk

Who is involved in Step One? The CEO with trusted advisors, but the CEO must lead.

Where does Step One take place? It's primarily an internal process that the CEO goes through.

How long does it take? It can be as quick as an instant or take as long as a lifetime.

I have stated many times in this book that healthcare liability is a risk that must be managed and that if it isn't, all manner of dire consequences may follow. You might be asking yourself, "What if these doom-and-gloom scenarios are nothing but hot air? Can this guy back up his grim prognosis?" Sure I can.

Let's take a look at some important facts:

- The cost of healthcare in the United States was an estimated $2.3 trillion in 2007. That works out to nearly $7,500 per person. And it's rising at the fastest rate in our history. By 2015, those costs are expected to jump to $4 trillion. That will represent 20 percent of the gross national product of the United States. *(The National Coalition on Health Care, www.nchc. org)*

- Since the year 2000, employment-based health-insurance premiums have gone up by about 87 percent. Each year, employers pay an average of $8,500 for a family's coverage. *(Henry J. Kaiser Family Foundation)*

- American employers are the largest source of health-insurance coverage for non-elderly Americans. *(2006–07 Survey of Wellness Programs at Business Roundtable Member Companies, Business Roundtable, www.businessroundtable.org)*

- A 2001 survey showed that 74 percent of private health-insurance spending is attributed to the 45 percent of privately insured Americans who suffer from one or more chronic conditions *(Partnership for Solutions, Johns Hopkins University, The Robert Wood Johnson Foundation, "Chronic Conditions: Making the Case for Ongoing Care, September 2004 Update")*

- Experts are now acknowledging the relationship between productivity and employees' health. They estimate that decreased productivity represents billions of dollars a year in lost revenue for American organizations. *(Institute of Health and Productivity Management, 1997)*

- In the future, employers may be forced to penalize people for unhealthy habits and poor lifestyle choices. *("Get Healthy—Or Else," BusinessWeek, February 26, 2007, p. 58)*

- Increasing physical activity directly increases productivity. It reduces mortality rates, on-the-job injuries, and chronic illness.

  (Harvard Alumni Study, American Academy of Health & Productivity Management, Centers for Disease Control)

- Over time, workplace wellness programs can result in savings averaging between 26 and 30 percent. There is an average return of $3 for every $1 spent by employers on wellness programs. This return can go as high as $6. The savings come from lower insurance costs, reduced absenteeism and increased productivity.

  (University of Michigan Health Management Research Center, "Cost Benefit Analysis and Report 2006")

Let's face it: Americans are fat, and they're just getting fatter. There's an obesity epidemic underway in this country, an epidemic that has hit the United States far harder than countries we have traditionally beaten in business. Obviously, this fact is hurting our competitiveness. American companies are losing business to foreign firms that have healthier and more productive workforces.

Our cost of healthcare insurance continues to rise. The January 2006 PriceWaterhouseCoopers report estimated an overall increase in premiums between 2004 and 2005 as 8.8 percent, which is much lower than the 13.7 percent increase reported in 2002, but also represents a 30 percent price increase in excess of inflation. The 2008 estimate is 7 percent over 2007's costs, while the economy is growing at only 4 percent—and this isn't going to change anytime soon unless corporate leaders and individual workers do something about the obesity epidemic that is directly related to increasing costs.

Corporations need to act quickly to institute change to their healthcare insurance systems. Individuals need to act quickly to take control of their personal health. Time is of the essence at both levels, and without prompt action, the situation will only get worse. The solution is not to throw more premium dollars at the problem or to turn it over to the government. The solution is education and the promotion of personal responsibility. And the effort must be led by the country's businesses and their top management.

The good news is that we can institute measures to bring healthcare costs under control. But in order to make positive changes, we have to take the first step: We must recognize the risk.

Step Two: Collect the Data

Who is involved in Step Two? The CEO, upper management, and the healthcare-plan risk-management consultant.

Where does Step Two take place? At the company offices.

How long does it take? Several weeks.

"All progress begins with the truth." These wise words were spoken by Dan Sullivan, founder and president of The Strategic Coach Inc.

In taking the first step of recognizing the risk, you're already acknowledging your awareness of some pretty frightening data. But that's only the beginning of the information gathering. Step Two requires you to collect as much data as possible on your employee population relative to their health and fitness so that you can quantify your risk. Data is collected through biometrics, health risk appraisals, and historical medical and pharmacy claims utilization data. You will also collect data on your current healthcare-plan design and provider networks. From this data, you will gain a clear picture of exactly what diseases and conditions are driving your healthcare costs and will be able to clearly recognize the savings that can be realized through effective healthcare-plan risk management.

Here are some interesting facts to keep in mind as you begin to collect data on your employee population:

- 70 percent of health risks are modifiable and can be reduced with lifestyle behavior changes.

- As you have already heard—and will continue to hear until we do something about it—obesity is out of control in this country. A recent study by the Duke University Medical Center has found that obese workers filed twice the number of workers' compensation claims, had seven times higher medical costs from those claims, and had missed thirteen times more days of work from injury or illness than non-obese workers.

- Absenteeism has become a huge roadblock to competitiveness and profits. Absenteeism, of course, brings productivity way down and can also bring healthcare costs way up.

- Not only do companies have to deal with absenteeism, but now there's also a growing problem of what we call presenteeism at the workplace. Presenteeism is when an employee shows up for work but performs below their ability because of poor health and fitness. It is considered to be a major factor in employee stress and distraction, as well as in loss of productivity.

Step Three: Ensure Organizational Readiness by Educating CEO and Staff

Who is involved in Step Three? The CEO, the best-practices insurance consultant, management (to complete their survey), and employees (to complete their survey).

Where does Step Three take place? Mainly in the head office, but throughout the company for completion of the survey.

How long does it take? This can depend on the size of the company but, on average, one month total. It takes about two weeks for the healthcare-plan risk-management consultant to conduct the cultural audit survey. It takes about a week for him or her to interview the upper management in one-on-one meetings. And it takes about another week to get back to the CEO with a final report that will be used as the basis of the implementation plan.

One of the first key things that a healthcare-plan risk-management consultant does when he or she comes into a company is conduct surveys to see how ready an organization is for change. I call these surveys the cultural audit, and in Part 2, I will go into detail about what these surveys entail.

Every company will of course be at a different level of readiness. With the information in hand about where a company falls on that spectrum, the CEO can begin the process of educating him- or herself and the employees to prepare them for the changes ahead.

There are a couple of key messages that a CEO needs to communicate to staff about why it's so urgent to take steps to contain the crisis in healthcare insurance. The first reason is the impact it's having on employees' lives, both now and for years to come. The second reason is the impact it's having on the business's bottom line.

When employees are overweight and out of shape, business suffers. Companies are beaten, over and over, by competitors who don't have to contend with high levels of absenteeism and presenteeism. When employees are fit and healthy, they're more productive and more creative. The workplace becomes a safer workplace with fewer accidents.

Now, making a profit is a great thing, and it's what keeps the engine of this country running. But many CEOs are not so single-minded that they don't care about the quality of life that their workers are experiencing. They recognize that their employees are their *most* valuable asset. And they recognize that these employees are human beings, not machines, and they deserve to lead full, healthy, and happy existences throughout their entire life spans.

Workers in the prime of their lives are already severely out of shape and overweight. Just imagine how these problems will intensify as these people age. Conditions that might appear manageable when these people are in their twenties explode into life-threatening diseases such as cancers, heart diseases, strokes, and diabetes. Their decline as they age will come much more rapidly than for people who are healthy and active. Instead of having a fulfilling retirement chasing the grandkids around, they will spend their time battling disease in a slow, painful decline.

The flip side of this equation is that people who have taken care of their health in their youth will have a much, much higher quality of life in their golden years. They will have the physical energy and stamina to devote time to their interests, hobbies, and passions. The wisdom and maturity that they have nurtured over the years is a valuable asset to our families and communities. We can't afford to lose out on the collective resources of our elders because they are getting sick and dying much sooner than they should.

Step Four: Assign This as Someone's Responsibility within Your Company

Who is involved in Step Four? CEO, upper management.

Where does Step Four take place? At the company headquarters.

How long does it take? A matter of days to assign this as someone's responsibility.

The CEO, of course, is the head of the company and has the ultimate responsibility for fixing the crisis of health-care insurance. Our evidence has shown time and again that when a CEO and his or her upper management are on board with a corporate wellness plan, there is a much, much higher success rate for the program among all of the company's employees.

But let's face it: The CEO is a busy person with an agenda that's packed full. It only makes sense to delegate the day-to-day management of the healthcare-plan risk-management program to someone from a company's upper management—or better yet, hire a healthcare-plan risk manager. This person will be the face of the corporate wellness program throughout the company. So it makes sense to have someone who is passionate and knowledgeable about wellness, someone who embodies its principles in both personal and professional life.

In some companies, like the fictional Midland Building Associates in our parable, it makes sense to have the risk manager who's already been handling safety issues also assume responsibility for a wellness program. Many of the objectives and the procedures cross over between safety and wellness.

But, ultimately, no matter who within a company is assigned to be in charge of corporate wellness, it is up to each individual worker to be responsible for his or her actions. Of course, workers already have a lot on their plates these days. Who doesn't? So it's good to give them a helping hand with measures such as financial incentives for people who stick with a fitness program. And financial disincentives are also important, such as ones for people who won't address a tobacco problem and are therefore costing their employers a lot more money in terms of healthcare.

Corporate wellness, as we've pointed out, is a very serious issue. But it's important that the pursuit of health and fitness be fun as well. So companies should consider initiatives such as friendly competitions between branches, departments, and regional offices. For example, they could have a corporate countdown to see who is losing the most weight. Internet technology and eye-catching computer interfaces can make these kinds of contests both fun and instructive at the same time.

Step Five: Build Partnerships

Who is involved in Step Five? The CEO, the best-practices insurance consultant, upper management, third-party vendors.

Where does Step Five take place? In the company's offices and throughout the country wherever the third-party vendors are located.

How long does it take? About three months to set up the specific details of a company's needs, on a case-by-case basis, based on the results of the cultural audit.

When a company has made it this far through the seven steps, it's already come a long way, and all the players deserve to give themselves a big pat on the back. But it's time now to bring in some outside experts to help manage the healthcare liability risk. These are highly trained third-party vendors, each one specializing in a different part of what is, admittedly, a complex process.

There are many advantages to be realized by a business that chooses to partner with a healthcare-plan risk-management firm. Healthcare-plan risk-management firms are able to group their clients and collectively contract with best-in-class service providers. They can

- leverage group purchasing power;
- implement best-in class risk-management techniques to impact claims; and
- share knowledge gained from the synergy of the group.

To use the specific example of Contractors Risk Management Services (CRMS), my company, these are some of the partnerships we've set up for our clients, all at significant discounts:

- CIGNA is the healthcare provider and network-claims administrator for our members.
- VitalSpring Technologies provides our claims-data management solutions. It supplies CRMS and all its members with a software tool that allows us to drill down into our claims data to determine what chronic

diseases and conditions are driving our claims so we can institute provocative measures to improve our performance.

- Kersh Wellness is the top-notch firm that handles the corporate wellness programs for CRMS clients.
- Towers Perrin does our actuarial work.

Again, these are just examples. But I think you're getting the picture of how partnerships and economies of scale with third-party vendors fit into the puzzle.

Step Six: Install the Programs and Procedures

Who is involved in Step Six? The CEO, upper management, all company employees with a domino, spill-over effect to their families as well.

Where does Step Six take place? Throughout the company in all its locations, with a domino effect into employees' homes and other places where they will pursue health and fitness (such as grocery stores, gyms, community centers, recreation trails, etc.).

How long does it take? The rollout throughout a company can be spread out over several weeks or several months, depending on its size. The initial information meeting with employees takes a couple of hours. The completion of their biometric testing and health-risk assessment takes about a week.

This is the stage at which a company's CEO and management rolls out, to all of their employees at all levels and in all locations, the new programs that they've been meticulously designing over the past three to four months. The top brass has already started the process of developing a culture of health and fitness, a process that makes the company ready to adopt and embrace change. Now, the CEO and management must communicate the message to each of their employees. The leadership of the company must drive the process so that every single worker feels engaged, both personally and professionally.

The actual rollout of the changes to healthcare insurance can be done in many different ways, of course. But what follows is a typical breakdown of what I've witnessed.

Employees will meet in groups at their workplace and hear a presentation from their leadership and from a wellness provider about how to improve their health, lower insurance costs and receive discounts on insurance premiums as an incentive. After that meeting, employees can sign up for the wellness program.

Trained staff from the wellness provider will carry out biometric testing to assess each employee's health profile. This will include a blood test and measurements of blood pressure, height, and weight. The employees will also complete a confidential health-risk assessment form that evaluates their current lifestyles as they pertain to nutrition, exercise, stress, etc.

Based on the results of the biometric testing and the health-risk assessment, the employees will be classified as low risk, medium risk, or high risk. If the employee is rated as high risk, he or she will be assigned a wellness advocate—that is, a qualified health consultant—who will begin working one-on-one with the employee to set personalized health and fitness goals.

This participation in the wellness program is also open to employees' spouses. It's usually voluntary to participate in this program in year one, but obviously the financial incentives as well as the examples of seeing colleagues and supervisors participate will be a key to boosting the sign-up rate.

Step Seven: Keeping Up the Program with Regular Maintenance

Who is involved in Step Seven? The CEO, upper management, and all employees, with a domino effect into their families and communities.

Where does Step Seven take place? Throughout the company in all its locales, with a domino effect into employees' homes, gyms, streets, schools, retirement homes, sidewalks, community centers, pools, bike trails, etc.

How long does it take? Every single day.

Congratulations! You've taken a big step and worked hard, and now you've reached the final stage in the process of taking control of your healthcare insurance costs. You can safely say that, by this point, you've negotiated your way out of a crisis. But now it's time for a regular maintenance plan to keep you on the right path.

Fortunately, there are many innovative, fun, and creative ways to keep the process in place and running strong.

Employees in the wellness program who have been identified as being high risk will begin an ongoing monthly telephone relationship with their wellness advocate. This consultant will help them keep track of health and fitness goals.

The employees who are low or medium risk will be responsible for their own health and fitness plan, by eating well, going to the gym, and so on.

All participants will have access to regular health meetings at their workplace. Messages about health and fitness in the workplace can be communicated in much the same way as messages about safety. It's a message that can be reinforced every day with posters at the workplace, pamphlets, fliers, and paycheck stuffers.

Employees who have experienced notable success in achieving their health and fitness goals can become mentors to their colleagues, just like Manny, the foreman at Cora Construction in our parable.

These success stories can also inspire media reports as well as DVD and video testimonials. At CRMS, we've created a set of engaging, humorous two-minute sketches, in both Spanish and English, which our clients can use at their health meetings. It's just one of the value-added services that a healthcare-plan risk-management firm can provide.

And these messages can be brought into workers' homes and shared with their families, extended families, housemates, and friends to communicate the benefits of wellness even more broadly into the community.

And, of course, there's the added motivation of financial incentives to keep participants in the wellness program on track. Each company can create a financial incentives program to fit its specific needs. What follows is the model we've used successfully at CRMS. It's based on a six-month cycle, and, remember, this is just one example.

At CRMS, for employees to qualify for a $300 reduction of their healthcare insurance premiums, participants in the wellness program must accumulate a minimum of 110 points over six months. This is how they can do it:

- A total of 10 points to complete the health risk assessment
- A total of 10 points to complete the biometric testing
- A total of 10 points for completing an annual physical examination
- A total of 20 points for being tobacco-free
- A total of 60 points for regular use of a KAM, a kinetic activity monitor that is worn on the belt like a pager. It measures the rate and intensity of all physical activity (except in water), and users enter the number of servings of fruit and vegetables consumed each day. To get the maximum of 10 points each month in this category, employees must register a KAM score of 10 points a day for at least 20 days out of that month.

We'd like to think that, with a great example set by a motivated CEO and management, close to 100 percent of employees would sign up for a new corporate wellness program once it is up and running. But, of course, real life isn't always as idealized as our expectations. It's only natural that participation rates will vary from company to company. And it's essential to keep the lines of communication open to employees who didn't initially sign up. Hopefully, after a year of seeing their colleagues and supervisors looking and feeling great, new people will sign up for the corporate wellness program in subsequent years.

The job of developing a culture of health and fitness in the workplace will be made easier from the very first step because everybody in the company—from the CEO down—will have more energy, creativity, and productivity.

It's not just a theory. It's a fact. When you eat well, exercise, cut out tobacco, and don't abuse alcohol and medication, you feel much better and have much more energy. Leading a full, productive, healthy life is everybody's responsibility. And everybody will win from getting on this road to change.

Part 2: Evaluating Your Readiness for Change

As I have explained in the previous section, once you've identified your risk and collected the data to back that up, a key part of the process of change is ensuring that your organization is ready to go through with it. Remember, that's Step Three of the seven steps.

There are different ways to ensure organizational readiness, but at CRMS, what we have found highly effective is administering organizational readiness surveys—what we call cultural audits—developed by our wellness partner, Kersh Wellness. Kersh Wellness is one of the top wellness providers in the United States and a constant, innovative leader in this ever-emerging field.

There are two distinct surveys that we use. One of them is administered only to client management. The second is administered to all client employees, including management. These results are first analyzed at Kersh Wellness and then shared with me and my staff. I then share the results of the cultural audit with the CEO and upper management of the client company. Together, we then develop an action plan.

Confidentiality is a key factor to keep in mind throughout *all* of the seven steps, but it might come to the forefront especially with measures like this survey that ask individuals to entrust some very personal information. Confidentiality of individuals is fervently maintained at all times, like a sacred trust. All information in the surveys is kept strictly confidential, and when the results are compiled, individuals can never be identified.

Although we highly recommend, of course, that you administer these surveys with a knowledgeable and skilled healthcare-plan risk-management consultant, it is informative and useful to be aware of the nature of these surveys.

For each of the two surveys, respondents identify their gender and their age range. Then they are asked to rate a series of statements on a scale of 1 to 5, with 1 representing a statement that they strongly disagree with and 5 being one that they strongly agree with.

SURVEY FOR MANAGEMENT

_____For the most part, heavy alcohol use is not common among employees.

_____Most employees are tobacco-free.

_____Employees are concerned with nutrition.

_____Employees are concerned with being healthy.

_____A wellness program would benefit the company.

_____A wellness program would benefit our employees.

_____Employees would be receptive to participating in a wellness program.

_____Employees generally seem to get along with each other.

_____Tension between management and non-management is not an issue for the company.

_____Upper management is responsive and communicates well with middle management/supervisors.

_____Management/supervisors communicate easily with non-management employees.

_____Upper management is willing to commit sufficient financial resources to a wellness program.

_____Employees don't worry about job security.

_____Our company does not have a high turn-
over rate.

_____Employees trust their immediate managers.

_____Employees are comfortable in approaching me if
they have a job-related problem.

_____Employees are comfortable in approaching me
if they have a personal problem that could affect
their job performance.

_____Our company adapts to change easily.

_____Our company places importance on being
flexible.

_____Policies and directives from upper management
are successfully communicated to employees.

_____Our company is dedicated to promoting healthy
lifestyles.

_____Problems in the company are openly addressed.

_____Stress levels in the workplace are manageable.

_____Our corporate structure is flat (there are rela-
tively few layers of management between upper
executives and entry-level employees).

_____Our company has experienced interpersonal problems in the recent past that have adversely affected the company.

_____Our company has experienced financial problems in the recent past that have adversely affected the company.

_____Our company has experienced labor problems in the recent past that have adversely affected the company.

_____If the company needs to take a new approach to an issue, management can admit that a current strategy isn't working.

SURVEY FOR ALL EMPLOYEES
(they identify whether they are management or not)

_____I believe my job is secure.

_____I believe that my company is open to positive change.

_____Management encourages employees to learn from mistakes.

_____My manager is easily approachable if I have a personal problem that could affect my job performance.

_____My immediate manager is trustworthy.

_____I believe my company cares about its employees.

_____My company does a good job of communicating with its employees.

_____In the past twelve months, I have tried to adopt a healthier lifestyle.

_____In the past twelve months, I have been successful in adopting a healthier lifestyle.

_____I believe participation in a wellness program would help me adopt a healthier lifestyle.

_____My coworkers discourage the use of tobacco.

_____My coworkers encourage eating healthy foods.

_____My coworkers discourage the abuse of alcohol.

_____My supervisor or manager discourages the use of tobacco.

_____My supervisor or manager encourages eating healthy foods.

_____My supervisor or manager discourages the abuse of alcohol.

_____My family members and/or housemates discourage the use of tobacco.

_____My family members and/or housemates encourage eating healthy foods.

_____My family members and/or housemates discourage the abuse of alcohol.

_____My coworkers support one another's efforts to adopt healthier lifestyles.

_____My family members and/or housemates support my efforts to adopt a healthier lifestyle.

_____My coworkers recognize one another's efforts to adopt healthier lifestyles.

_____My family members and/or housemates recognize my efforts to adopt a healthier lifestyle.

_____My family members and/or housemates encourage me to exercise regularly.

_____My immediate supervisor or manager encourages me to be physically active.

_____I believe routine medical screenings are important in maintaining good health.

_____My company provides employees with opportunities to engage in healthy lifestyle activities.

_____My company recognizes employees for adopting healthy lifestyles.

_____My company rewards employees for adopting healthy lifestyles.

_____My company is dedicated to promoting healthy lifestyles.

_____My company promotes a feeling of community.

_____In the past year, I have attempted to lose weight.

_____In the past year, I have attempted to increase exercise.

_____In the past year, I have attempted to manage stress.

Survey Evaluation

Obviously, I believe that evaluation of these organizational readiness surveys is best done with the skill and expertise of wellness experts and a healthcare-plan risk-management consultant. But just by looking at the questions, you get the gist of where they are going. They are identifying the level of awareness of key wellness concepts such as proper nutrition, exercise, and stress management, as well as the ill effects of tobacco use, alcohol abuse, prescription drug abuse, etc.

On the management side, they are looking at key aspects of corporate culture such as openness to change, levels of communication, etc.

Obviously, if a company has a high level of awareness about wellness to begin with and an openness to change among its management, then going through the seven steps will be a much easier process. But that is not to say that it's a lost cause for companies that don't have that level of awareness to begin with. Of course not. Nobody should throw up his or her hands in defeat and just walk away from such an important task. It's merely that identifying the extent of any obstacles at the outset is a key factor in properly planning and implementing the seven steps of change.

Part 3: Nutrition: A Key Ingredient of Wellness

It might seem like a no-brainer to say that food is one of the basic necessities of life. The air we breathe, the water we drink, the food we eat—no human being can exist without it.

But the tragic state of affairs in America in the twenty-first century is this: Not only have we forgotten how to eat properly, but we have actually gone so far in the other direction that we are poisoning ourselves through what we eat. We are missing out on key nutrients—gifts that the bounty of the earth is offering us—through what we're not eating, and we are actually killing ourselves through what we *are* eating.

We are such a rich country with such a plentiful supply of food that we have fallen into the very dangerous habit of eating way too much, way too often. It's an ironic fact of this crisis that a seemingly good thing—our abundance of food—is causing terrible damage. All great civilizations have struggled with prosperity. I'd like to think that we are smart enough to handle it.

So many people are eating fast food and convenience food nearly all of the time just because they don't have the time or the energy for the extra effort that's involved in shopping, cooking, and cleaning up. And this convenience food is basically poison to our systems. It's full of bad fats, bad sugars, way too much salt, and additives that have been linked to cancers, heart disease, and a whole raft of other illnesses. Gigantic, supersized portions, which cost mere pennies to fast-food chains, are making junkies out of Americans and leading to overwhelming rates of obesity, the likes of which we've never experienced.

Home-cooked meals are often the exception rather than the rule for most Americans. I mean real home-cooked meals where everything is made from scratch. Even with the seemingly home-cooked meals we get now, many of the elements are processed in some way. And food processed in the wrong way strips it of its natural nutrients and can also change the chemical composition of food so that something that is theoretically good for us can become bad.

Take bread, for instance—the most basic foodstuff there is and one on which entire civilizations depended as a staple nutrient. Why is it that nowadays we've come to think of bread as being a bad thing, a bad carb that some of those trendy diets tell us we have to cut out of our lives completely? It's actually a result of how a lot of bread is manufactured and the impact this has on how our bodies process food.

Our bodies need whole grains. Our bodies need fiber. And the trendy diets that say we should stop eating bread are wrong. But with much of the commercially made bread—i.e., those made with refined white flour—the fiber is lost, as are the essential fatty acids and most of the vitamins and minerals. And all of these nutrients that are good for us have been replaced with other elements, not only preserving agents, but also partially hydrogenated oils, coloring, mold inhibitors, firming agents, and refined sugars. So what this has done is change the chemical composition of the bread entirely, and, as a result, our bodies' way of processing it has changed entirely too.

This new kind of bread (just to follow through with the same example, but it's true of other foodstuffs too) can result in our bodies' producing too much insulin to process it. And when our bodies do that too often, we become insulin-resistant. This may lead to metabolic syndrome, which can then lead to diabetes.

And you have to factor in the obesity element as well. With our example of the overprocessed bread, as with examples of many foodstuffs, it's not clear what comes first, the chicken or the egg. Does bad food lead to obesity? Or is overeating leading to the breakdown of our bodies' ability to process food? It's a vicious cycle; that much is clear. And it's time we break out of it.

The other really tragic thing about American eating habits is how we have come to neglect fruits and vegetables. This makes no sense when study after study shows us the unique vitamins, nutrients, and disease-fighting elements that fresh produce provides, which no vitamin supplement in the world can replicate.

It's crazy to think that something as simple as eating fresh fruit and vegetables has fallen by the wayside in contemporary America. The most recent nutritional recommendations of the US Department of Agriculture, represented in the food pyramid, maintain that an average person on a 2,000-calorie diet needs to consume four servings (two cups) of fruit a day and five servings (two-and-a-half cups) of vegetables. And most Americans aren't even coming close. Are they intimidated because they have only a vague idea of what a serving is? It's really a small and manageable amount, just half a cup. So there is absolutely no excuse not to get your apple a day, and then some!

Part 4: Further Resources

As I have mentioned before, there is a ton of fantastic material available today about health, fitness, and wellness, both on the Internet and in print. Obviously, I can't list everything, but I wanted to make a few suggestions to get you started on your own personal quest to deepen your knowledge of a very important subject that affects your life every hour of every day, as well as the lives of your loved ones. Every effort has been made to ensure accuracy, but please keep in mind that the names of websites do change, and certain books do go out of print.

There's also some blank space at the end of this section to record your own definitions and interesting data that you have come across in your own exploration on the theme of wellness.

Happy research!

Books

The Culprit & The Cure: Why Lifestyle Is the Culprit Behind America's Poor Health and How Transforming That Lifestyle Can Be the Cure
Steven G. Aldana, Ph.D.
Maple Mountain Press (2005)

Younger Next Year: Live Strong, Fit, and Sexy—Until You're 80 and Beyond
Chris Crowley and Henry S. Lodge, M.D.
Workman Publishing Co. (2007)

Younger Next Year for Women: Live Strong, Fit, and Sexy—Until You're 80 and Beyond
Chris Crowley and Henry S. Lodge, M.D.
Workman Publishing Co. (2007)

Worksite Wellness, Cost Benefit Analysis and Report, 1979 to 2006, University of Michigan, Health Management Research Center

Internet Tools

The US Department of Agriculture's My Pyramid site
www.mypyramid.gov

American Heart Association
www.americanheart.org

American Diabetes Association
www.diabetes.org

American Construction Benefits Group
www.acbg.net

A great calorie-counting tool is www.dietpower.com. It trains users on nutrition and proper portion size.

Some other great websites:

www.smallstep.com
www.webMD.com
www.justmove.org
www.fruitsandveggiesmatter.gov

Conclusion

I've talked a lot about wellness in this book. Maybe it's a term you've heard before, or maybe this is the first time you've come across it. One thing is certain: You're going to be hearing a lot more about wellness in the years and decades to come.

For CEOs and employees alike, the key to taking control of your health and the rising costs of healthcare is in your hands. I hope you've found lots of food for thought in the parable and in the seven steps of change outlined in this book.

I hope it's inspired you to imagine how you can make a difference in both your life and the lives of others. A lot of simple steps can add up to making a monumental difference in both your own physical and emotional health and in the economic well-being of your workplace.

Take the stairs instead of the elevator, at least some of the time.

Replace vending machines crammed with junk food with nutritious food.

Know how to buy a quick nutritious lunch at a convenience store if you're running short on time.

Learn how to read a food label.

Sit down and enjoy a home-cooked meal with family or friends.

Eat an apple.

Ride a bike.

But the very first step is having the vision to embrace change. And if you've come this far in the book, you already have that. Congratulations, and keep on the right track. You'll start to notice the difference and to feel better immediately. It's guaranteed.

Acknowledgments

The Father, Son and Holy Spirit, for your love, guidance, grace, and mercy.

My wife, Risa (my much better half), for your love, kindness, and patience. My daughter, Kimberly, for your love, compassion, and your commitment to doing your best. My son, Eric, for your love, tenacity, and commitment to doing your best.

My parents, Lloyd (recently departed) and Esther Heussner, for showing me how to love and live. For setting an example with their hard work and dedication while running the family businesses.

My in-laws, Leon (recently departed) and Louise Smith, for being the best in-laws a person could ask for.

My siblings, Candace Preston, Michele Mahood, Bob Heussner, Marilee Barnett, and Mark Heussner, each of whom is so unique and special in his or her own way, for your love and for the excellent example that you have set for me.

Dr. Jude Ndudi, one of the smartest businesspeople that I know, for being a great friend and for setting a great example.

Dr. Terry James, Richard Kersh, Melbourne O'Banion, Dr. Bill Titus, and the rest of the team at Kersh Wellness, for your valuable insight and your willingness to take risks.

Bill McIntyre, for being a great friend, coach, and mentor.

The team at American Construction Benefits Group and Contractors Risk Management Services, for your hard work and dedication. And the members of ACBG, RRG – JD Abrams, Duininck Companies, Jaynes Companies, Nabholz, Phillips & Jordan, and Total Risk Management.

My friends in Dan Sullivan's Strategic Coach program, a powerful group of entrepreneurs, for your energy, thought, and creativity.

Dr. Jeff Warren, for being a friend and for setting a great example.

The great coaches and mentors that I have had in life (forgive me if I've left anyone out): Lloyd Heussner, Rich Adams, Ernestine Beauchamp, Bill Bonini, Mark Carrow, Jerry Coates, Tom Doane, Darrell Dodson, Frank Engraff, Al Goldstein, Phil Hildebrand, Dick Hull, Mel Isaacs, Mark Koskovich, Marty Lindberg, Mike McCann, Bill Miller, Gary Mottershead, Sam Mullis, Al Pearman,

George Reck, Mike Reeves, John Seckinger, Gary Simpson, Dan Sullivan, Jackie Thomas, Jeff Thomas, Reg Titcombe, Darrin Weber, and Dan White.

Chuck Lee, Carl Cudworth, and Charles Chen at Towers Perrin.

Shreedhar Potaratsu, Denise Gauthier, Tom Shattenfield and the team at VitalSpring Technologies.

Jack Gibson, Paul Murray, and Rob Olson at International Risk Management Institute.

Raleigh Roussell and his team at Quoin.

Toby Cummings and his team at the Associated Builders & Contractors (ABC).

Tom Johnson and his team at the Associated General Contractors (AGC of Texas).

My friends in the Construction Financial Management Association (CFMA).

The customers of Heussner Insurance Agency, Inc., for making business a pleasure.

My snow-skiing buddies, Roger Blaser, John Bodnar, Rob Boomer, Greg Brown, Tony Childress, John Cleary, Vince DeAngelis, Mike DeRuby, Neil Dostie, Paul Holden, Tom Holden, Mike Kirlin, Steve LaMure, Robert McCann, Paul Messenger, Paul Moore, David Moreland, Kirk Quaschnick, Kevin Richardson, Greg Thompson . . . for doing your best to keep up.

My golfing buddies, Bill Reeg, Guy Banks, Greg Brown, Grady Dickens, Dave Chase, Paul Holden.

Tommy Zinna, for getting me back into playing hockey.

Ross Slater, Susan Hart and the team at Highspot Inc.

I would like to extend special thanks to Richard Kersh and Dr. Jude Ndudi for their important contributions to the writing of this book. Without them, this book would not have been possible.

About the Author

Steve Heussner is passionate about helping companies and their employees become as healthy and productive as they can be.

He is the founder and president of American Construction Benefits Group, Ltd. (ACBG), a captive insurance company that issues contractual indemnity insurance to its member companies. He is also the founder of Contractors Risk Management Services, Inc. (CRMS), which provides employee benefit risk-management services to contractors.

Steve began his career as a financial analyst before becoming an insurance agent in 1988. Over the years, Steve has won numerous company and industry awards. In 1996, he formed his own insurance agency. He holds a degree in Geological Engineering from Princeton University.

Steve is a member of the Million Dollar Round Table, the National Association of Insurance and Financial

Advisors, and the Construction Financial Management Association. He serves on the leadership, insurance, and legislative committees of the Texas Branch of the Associated General Contractors (AGC), Highway, Heavy, Utilities & Industrial Branch, and is active in Quoin, the Dallas/East Texas and Fort Worth branch of the AGC, as well as many other industry groups and initiatives.

Steve and his wife, Risa, live in McKinney, Texas, with their children, Eric and Kimberly. Steve enjoys weight training, running, cycling, ice hockey, skiing, cooking, reading, and public speaking.